COUNTING STARS

David Almond

First published in Great Britain by
Hodder Children's Books 2000
This Large Print edition published by
BBC Audiobooks by arrangement with
Hodder Children's Books 2006

ISBN 10: 1 4056 6103 8
ISBN 13: 978 1 4056 6103 4

British Library Cataloguing in Publication Data available

Printed and bound in Great Britain by
Antony Rowe Ltd., Chippenham, Wiltshire

For all of us
James, Catherine, Colin, David,
Catherine, Barbara, Mary, Margaret

CONTENTS

INTRODUCTION

These stories are about my childhood. They're about the people I grew up with, our hopes and fears, our tragedies and joys. They explore a time that has disappeared and a place that has changed. They bring back those who have gone, and allow them to walk and speak again within the pages of a book. Like all stories, they merge memory and dream, the real and the imagined, truth and lies. And, perhaps like all stories, they are an attempt to reassemble what is fragmented, to rediscover what has been lost.

THE MIDDLE OF THE WORLD

She started with The Universe. Then she wrote The Galaxy, The Solar System, The Earth, Europe, England, Felling, Our House, The Kitchen, The White Chair With A Hundred Holes Like Stars, then her name, Margaret, and she paused.

'What's in the middle of me?' she asked.

'Your heart,' said Mary.

She wrote My Heart.

'In the middle of that?'

'Your soul,' said Catherine.

She wrote My Soul.

Mam reached down and lifted the front of Margaret's T-shirt and prodded her navel.

'That's where your middle is,' she said. 'That's where you were part of me.'

Margaret drew a row of stick figures, then drew concentric rings growing out from each of them.

'Where's the real middle of the

1

world?' she said.

'They used to think the Mediterranean,' said Catherine. 'Medi means middle. Terra means world. The sea at the middle of the world.'

Margaret drew a blue sea with a green earth around it.

'There was another sea at the edges,' said Catherine. 'It was filled with monsters and it went right to the end of the world. If you got that far, you just fell off.'

Margaret drew this sea. She put fangs and fins for monsters.

'There's no end, really, is there?' she said.

'No,' said Catherine.

'And there's no middle, is there?'

Catherine laughed.

'Not really.'

Mam prodded Margaret's navel again.

'That's the middle of the world,' she said.

*   *   *

Later that day we went to the grave.

Colin rushed home from Reyrolle's on his Vespa for lunch. He bolted his food and rattled away again. We heard the scooter taking him on to Felling Bank and down towards the square.

When it faded, Mary said,

'Should we go to the grave today?'

We hadn't been for months. We thought of the dead being in Heaven rather than being in the Earth.

'Good idea,' said Mam. 'I'll make some bara brith for when you get home.'

We were on the rocky path at the foot of the street when Dandy ran after us. He was a little black poodle that was never clipped and had horrible breath.

'Go home!' said Mary. 'Dandy, go home!'

He yapped and growled and whined.

'Dandy, go home!'

No good. We just had to let him trot along beside us. Margaret fiddled with her navel as she walked.

'When I started,' she said, 'what was I like?'

'What do you think you were like?'

3

said Mary. 'Like a gorilla? You were very very very little. You were that little, you couldn't even be seen. You were that little, nobody even knew you were blinkin there!'

'Daft dog,' said Catherine, as Dandy ran madly through a clump of foxgloves and jumped at bees.

Soon we saw Auntie Jan and Auntie Mona ahead of us. They wore head scarves and carried shopping bags on their arms.

'Bet you can't tell which is which,' said Mary.

'Even when they're talking to me I can't tell which is which,' said Margaret.

The two aunts hurried into Ell Dene Crescent.

'Did they look the same when nobody knew they were there?' said Margaret.

'Of course they did!' said Mary. 'Everybody looks the same when they can't be blinkin seen!'

The aunts waved and grinned and we all waved and Dandy yapped and then they hurried on again down into Ell

Dene Crescent.

Mary picked daisies from the verges as we walked.

She said, 'Dad once said that daisies were the best of all flowers. I think I remember that.'

'You do,' said Catherine. 'You do remember. He called them day's eyes. Awake in the day and closed asleep at night.'

Further on, Daft Peter lay in his greatcoat under a tree on The Drive.

'Not him!' said Catherine. 'We'll never get away from him!'

We sat on a bench on Watermill Lane.

'How far is it?' said Margaret.

'You know how far,' said Mary.

'Nowhere's far in Felling,' said Catherine.

We watched Daft Peter.

'Move,' said Catherine. 'Go on. Move.'

'Is Felling very small?' said Margaret.

Mary stamped her feet.

'Yes,' said Catherine.

'Is it the smallest place in the world?'

'Is this Daft Question Day?' said Mary.

'Yes!' said Margaret.

'It's very small,' said Catherine. 'But there's smaller places.'

'Where?'

'Places in the desert,' said Mary. 'Rings of huts in the jungle. Villages in the Himalayas.'

'Yes,' said Catherine. 'And places like Hebburn or Seaton Sluice.'

'Not Seaton Sluice,' said Mary. 'It's got that big beach. It's got to be bigger than Felling. And Hebburn's got that big new shopping centre.'

Catherine sighed.

'Windy Nook, then,' she said.

'That's not fair,' said Mary. 'Windy Nook's a part of somewhere else.'

'Where, then? And make it somewhere we know.'

'Bill Quay,' said Mary.

No one said anything, even though we all knew Bill Quay was part of somewhere else as well.

'Thank goodness,' said Catherine. 'Bill Quay.'

Daft Peter didn't move. In the end,

we walked on. Dandy snarled as we drew nearer to the man.

'Dandy!' said Catherine.

Daft Peter smiled and rubbed his eyes.

'Here's me thought I was dreamin,' he said. 'And all the time I'm just wakin up.'

He leaned against the tree.

'What would ye say if I knew how to turn swimmin fish into flyin fowl?' he said.

'Take no notice,' whispered Catherine.

'Nowt much at all, I see,' said Peter. 'But what if I said I could take you girls and show you how to fly aroond this tree.'

'I'd say you couldn't!' said Mary.

'Aha!' said Peter. 'Just let me look inside this bag, then.'

He dug into a brown carrier bag. He took out a sandwich, something bright red and black hanging out of two dried-out slices of bread. He held it out to Mary as we approached.

'Take a bite of that,' he said. 'Gan on, take a bite of that and see.'

7

Dandy jumped up at him, barking and snarling. Daft Peter flailed and kicked and the sandwich flew into the road.

'Daft dog!' he shouted. 'Look what ye've done to me dinna!'

We hurried past.

'What would ye say if I turned a daft dog into a nice meat pie?' yelled Peter.

'I'd say it would be very hairy and it would stink!' said Mary.

We arrived at the high steel graveyard gates. Just inside, withered flowers and broken wreaths were heaped in bins. Wasps and flies hovered and crawled. We held Dandy back from jumping at them. We all agreed that simple daisies were the best idea. We walked in single file on the narrow path between the graves. We murmured the names, the familiar and the unknown. At the far edge, just beyond the spiked fence, traffic thundered on the bypass.

We stood before our grave: Barbara, *beloved* sister, 1959; James, *beloved father, 1966; Neither can they die any* more, *for they are equal unto the angels;*

and the empty area for other names. Mary placed the daisies by the headstone. We hung our heads and said our prayers. We said the prayers that Mam and Colin would have said. I imagined the two crumbled coffins and bodies, their intermingled dust. I imagined the new coffins being placed there, the new names being written, the new dust mingling. Not enough room to take all of us, not enough space for all of our names.

'What did she look like?' said Mary, as always.

'She was lovely,' said Catherine, as always. 'She looked a bit like all of us.'

'I love her,' said Margaret. 'And I never even saw her.'

'You remember Dad, though,' said Catherine. 'You can both see Dad.'

'Yes,' they said.

We dried our eyes and wandered among the graves. The untouched ground between the graves and the bypass was narrowing.

'Where will they *put* everybody?' said Mary.

Nobody knew.

9

'Maybe they go back to the start,' said Catherine, and we looked across the neat rows towards St Mary's church a quarter mile away, where the trees and the tilting faded gravestones were.

'It must have been lovely once,' Mary said. 'The little church and a few graves and none of the noise.'

As we walked back towards the gates, Margaret said,

'Are all the people here in Heaven like Dad and Barbara are?'

'Lots of them,' said Catherine.

'Heaven must be very big,' said Margaret.

'It must be blinkin enormous,' said Mary.

We walked through the stink of the flowers. Daft Peter waited outside against the graveyard wall. He swigged something from a black bottle.

We crossed the road and kept away from him.

'Have a sip of this!' he yelled. 'This'll get ye flyin!'

We heard the shuffle of his feet behind us as we turned on to The Drive. Dandy kept pausing, turning, snarling. Margaret kept on fiddling with her navel.

'Here!' yelled Peter. 'What would ye say if I said I knew where the entrance to Hell is?'

'I would say you were Daft Peter,' whispered Mary.

'What's that?' yelled Peter. 'What would ye say? Eh? Eh?' Catherine sighed. She turned around. Dandy stood at her side, snarling.

'I'd say you were wrong and you don't and you should think more about the way up to Heaven. Now go away.'

Peter swigged from his bottle.

'Aha!' he said. 'Ahahaha! And what would ye say if I said if you went to Felling Square and went to the fountain and looked doon through the cracks in the pavements that ye'd soon get to feel the heat and smell the sulphur and see the fire and the Devil hisself waitin to welcome ye?'

Dandy snarled.

'Nowt much, I see,' said Peter.

We walked on.

'Cat got your tongues, eh?'

'That dog got me dinna!' he yelled.

11

Margaret giggled.

'Aha!' yelled Peter. 'And what would ye say if I said the top of that fountain's shaped just like a little lass's belly button?'

Margaret snapped her T-shirt down.

'Get him, Dandy!' said Mary, and Dandy rushed at Peter again. Peter kicked and flailed and his drink sprayed and splashed out of the top of the bottle. The dog trotted proudly back to us.

'There now,' said Mary. 'That's fettled him.'

'That dog got me dinna an me drink!' yelled Peter.

We giggled and sighed.

Auntie Mona came out of Ell Dene Crescent carrying her shopping bag.

'Just popping down for some bread for the tea,' she said. 'And are you all all right?'

She saw Peter.

'Daft soul,' she said. 'Has he been pestering you?'

'That dog got me dinna!' yelled Peter.

Auntie Mona giggled.

12

'Is that right?' she said.

'Aye!' said Peter. 'What would ye say if I said that dog got me dinna?'

Auntie Mona took out her purse. She held out some pennies to him.

Peter shuffled meekly towards her and took the coins.

'There,' she said. 'Get yourself a pie from Myers and stop pestering people.'

Peter closed his lips tight and shuffled away towards Felling Square.

'Poor daft soul,' said Auntie Mona.

'Aha!' he yelled. 'And what would ye say if I said the best pies is from Dickman's?'

Auntie Mona laughed and said she had to get off. They'd soon be back for their tea. She hurried away.

'Which one was that?' said Margaret.

'Auntie Jan,' said Mary.

'No,' said Catherine. 'Auntie Mona.'

Beside the rocky path, Dandy chased the bees again.

'What *would* you say if Daft Peter knew those things?' said Margaret.

'I'd say it was Daft Question Day,' said Mary.

We looked back over the hundreds

of houses towards the graveyard.

Catherine said, 'Maybe Heaven doesn't have to be so big. They said at school that sometime soon the number of people alive will be more than all the people who've ever lived.'

We pondered this while Dandy rushed madly through the foxgloves.

'It's nice to think they're there together, isn't it?' said Mary.

'Yes,' we said.

Dandy trotted home and disappeared. At the gate we smelt the bara brith baking.

'Did you say a prayer for me?' said Mam.

'Yes,' we said.

'And I put daisies on the grave,' said Mary.

'They'd like that.'

She took the bara brith out of the oven and laid it on a wire rack to cool. I sat on the back step with Catherine and we looked out at the immensity of the sky. Margaret sat on the White Chair With A Hundred Holes Like Stars and drew herself and Catherine and Mary flying around Felling's trees.

Mary told Mam about Dandy, Daft Peter, Auntie Mona and Auntie Jan. We heard Colin's scooter rattling up Felling Bank and turning into the street. He roared into the garden, and pulled his parka and his helmet off as he came into the house.

Then we all sat at the little table in the bright kitchen. We ate huge slices of the warm bread, sighed at the sweetness of sultanas, caught the melting butter with our tongues, squeezed in tight at the middle of the world.

COUNTING THE STARS

Each year Father O'Mahoney told us about the stars. He told us at the year's end, when the oldest of us were about to leave St John's and go up to St Joseph's. Each time it was the same. He stood in the school hall in his black clothes with the single band of white about his throat to give us his prayers, his congratulations and his warnings. When he spoke of knowledge he made a fist and glared down at the leavers in the front row below him.

'You will come upon those who will tell you everything is knowable,' he said. 'Those who will look into the night and say they can tell you the number of the stars. Turn away from them. It is a blasphemy for man to feign knowledge of what can be known only to God.'

One year one of us, either in mischief or in search of catechismic certainties, was bold enough to raise his hand.

16

'Father, how many stars can I count before it becomes a sin?'

The priest was silent for a moment.

'It is beyond a hundred that the sin begins to deepen, my son. Beyond a hundred and your soul begins to darken. Beyond a hundred and you take your very life in your hands.'

He paused again, contemplating his answer.

'Yes,' he murmured. 'Beyond a hundred. That's about the time.'

And for ever after, this precise and local doctrine was repeated and became our lore.

*   *   *

On glittering autumn nights, I made a circle of my thumb and forefinger and peered through into the dozens and dozens of stars in that small space. I compared the smallness of this circle with the vastness all around and understood the huge potential of the night for blasphemy and death. My friends and I would tantalise and tempt ourselves when darkness ended our

17

football games and we sprawled on the cold grass and our breath rose in plumes and vapour curled from the exposed skin of our hands and legs.

Ninety, one would begin, pointing upward, passing it on to the next in line. *Ninety-one . . . ninety-two . . . ninety-three . . .* Our fright was disguised with giggles and curses, but we were truly in fear and trembling if ever the boldest among us began to speak the fateful numbers beyond ninety-nine.

*   *   *

As I grew older, of course, and once I'd left St John's myself, I soon saw through this subterfuge: the attempts of an old Irish priest to stifle the liberating effects that education might have on our minds, to keep us in a state of obeisance and fright before his worn-out religion. In my new school, I plunged happily into the intricacies of number and computation. I learned that the earth existed in an obscure corner of an obscure galaxy in what for all we knew might be an obscure universe in a universe of universes. I learned the potential endlessness of all numbers. I knew the numbers of our nearest stars and the distances between them. I peered through binoculars from my bedroom window and saw the stars beyond the stars, and I counted them, and ignored the impossibility of numbering individuals.

'One million,' I whispered. 'Two million . . .'

Sometimes, from his bed three feet away from mine, my brother Colin would whisper and complain.

'What the hell you doing?'

'Nothing. Just counting. Three million. Four million . . .'

It exasperated him. He had dismissed such childish nonsense years ago while I experienced each time the thrill of my transgression. My voice was steady and bold in the small room. I knew by now that it was the smallness of our brains, rather than the wrath of God, that kept our understanding in thrall.

*   *   *

I was fourteen when it was my oldest sister Catherine's turn to leave St John's. At the end of her last day I made sure I was at the garden gate to greet her.

'O'Mahoney's been blathering about the stars,' I said.

'*Father* O'Mahoney,' she said.

I laughed at the word.

'Father! Anyway, don't believe him. I bet he warned you about counting.'

She shrugged.

'It's nonsense. I'll show you tonight.'

That night I waited for the long summer dusk to end and for true darkness to fall. I tiptoed to her room. I shuffled past Mary and Margaret's bed. I woke her and we knelt on her bed and leaned on the windowsill and pressed our faces close to the pane. We heard the gentle breathing of our parents as they slept next door. I began in the lowest corner of the sky, pointing down over the rooftops of our estate to the sky above St Patrick's steeple, and began to count. My finger ticked off

20

the amounts above our small town, leaving untouched the huge expanse of universe beyond. She began to tremble as the numbers mounted.

'Don't,' she whispered.

I held her as she began to pull away. I grinned as I counted more quickly and ran the numbers together in a blur.

'Hundred,' I said at last. 'Hundred and one, hundred and two, hundred and three. See?'

I saw the stars reflected in her eyes, how they shone among her tears. We heard Mary and Margaret stirring. I leaned down and touched the young girls' heads.

'It's nothing,' I whispered. 'Go back to sleep.'

I touched Catherine's head, too.

'Are you all right?' I said.

She didn't answer.

I told her she was too young now, but one day she'd understand.

I tiptoed back to my room.

I lay looking out into the night. I cursed myself.

'Forgive me,' I said into the silence, before descending into my rationalist's dreams.

*   *   *

Soon afterwards, our father became ill. He stayed in his bed. He had time off work. There was trouble in his groin, then in his back, his chest. In the night we heard his baffled exclamations of pain. He was taken to hospital where the speed of his decline simply accelerated. He lay pale-faced on the white bed and stared astonished at us and our mother. He licked his dried-out lips. His voice faded to a whisper: *What the hell's going on?*

They opened him to see what was inside and they quickly closed him again. He was sent back to us with a piece of his lung removed. He told us the worst was over. Their bed was put in the front living-room downstairs. Now the house was filled with the rasping of his breath, Mam's desperately comforting whispers.

'What's wrong?' we asked her.

She shook her head. An infection. Not what had been expected. Nothing.

He would get better now.

'What had it been?' we asked.

She shook her head again. Nothing. A mystery. She turned her eyes away.

In the evenings he sat among us in his dressing gown. Often he asked me to rub his back with ointments. The room filled with the scents of Ralgex or Deep Heat while I ran my fingers over his flesh, his ribs and spine, feeling each time how the skin was gathered closer to the bone, and learning how the source of pain each time was more elusive.

He yelped and stiffened and sighed with gratitude.

'That's better, son,' he whispered. 'Rub it all away.'

When nothing worked and it became unbearable, Mam would send Colin or me running down to the Bay Horse for brandy and we knew moments of joy those nights when he was tipsy enough to go beyond the pain and tell us of how it would be once he was well again. We complied in this comforting fiction. We sat in a circle around him and kept our eyes from those of our mother, from the truth that was so dark and deep and obvious beneath the bright surface of her smiles.

The year darkened. All autumn, Mary and Margaret kept being sent away to stay with our grandparents. The doctor and the priest became familiar visitors in the house. Father O'Mahoney would rest his great hand on my head.

'You must pray very hard,' he would tell me, and I would answer, 'Yes, Father,' as he stepped out into the night.

*   *   *

Christmas approached, with sleet and huge dull clouds hanging over everything. Mary and Margaret dropped notes behind the gas fire, requests for presents and for Daddy to be well again. They prepared a card for him: vivid blue night, single perfect five-pointed star shining on the Holy Family. In deeper ignorance than any of us, they scanned the sky and lamented the gloom up there.

'How will he see through that?' they asked. 'How will he ever find his way to us?'

All of us were asked to go to our grandparents for Christmas Day. We sat around Dad's bed eating chocolate and taking sips of his sherry and pulling presents from stockings, then he and Mam kissed us all in turn as we went out.

Colin kept us in order as we took the short walk through the quiet streets. 'They need this special day together,' he explained as we followed him. 'A day of rest to keep him getting better.' We admired the girls' new shoes, the brilliant patent shine on them. We heard distant carols pouring from radios. We smelt Christmas dinners, saw the families behind the windows. Catherine showed us the beautiful long silvery clouds, the moon still shining alongside the sun even though it was day. We entered the other house to huge embraces, pillowcases filled with gifts.

We returned at dusk, when frost glittered like starlight on the pavements. He was sleeping, Mam drowsed in the chair by the bed. The steel sick bowl lay by his pillow. He was pallid, grey-yellow; the pyjama top hung loosely over his bones. He woke up for a moment as Mam whispered about their day together, how joyous he'd been, how he'd loved the food, how he'd asked what time we'd return. He stared at us in amazement, then touched Mam on her arm and asked us, 'Do you understand you're in the presence of one of God's chosen angels?'

*   *   *

Then Boxing Day, and the doctor, and Mary and Margaret sent away again, and Father O'Mahoney as the light failed, blacker than ever in his suit and with the black-fringed stole hanging over his shoulders and the white host in his pocket and the darkness in his eyes. From the front living-room we heard the insistent murmur of Latin, we caught the scent of the anointing oil.

When the priest left, he spanned my

head with his hand again, and could say nothing, and I pressed upward to him, searching for the strength and comfort in him.

Then just Dad's breathing, his groans, Mam's eternal comforting.

It was Catherine who heard him die. She was in her bedroom above him. I was somewhere in the house, head ringing with prayers and appeals to God, to Jesus, His mother and all the Saints, to anything that might make things as they were again. She told me years later that she heard the final gasping of his breath below, then silence, nothing, and she knew it was over.

*   *   *

Their bed was removed and his coffin brought in and all the days he lay there I was unable to make myself go in to him. The house teemed with visitors: our boundless relatives; the Legion of Mary; the Knights of St Columba; the Women's League. Father O'Mahoney came time and again. The Brothers of

St Vincent de Paul gathered in the garden then poured in from the dark and the house shuddered at their chanting of the rosary. All week Mam sat white-faced, gracious, miraculously calm. Then he was taken away and Colin and I served at the funeral in white robes and we all splashed holy water into the earth after him and chanted the prayers and threw handfuls of dirt and wafted the smoke of incense over him. Afterwards in the crowded house tender words were repeated and repeated. He was at peace now. He would be looking down on us with love. A day would come when all of us would meet again. Aunties tended to us, two of Dad's sisters, the dark-haired identical twins. Mary and Margaret in bright new dresses and their shining new shoes squeezed in at Mam's sides. There were many tears, and some laughter as my father's sisters and brothers talked of his childhood. Then dusk deepened, and one by one and group by group the guests began to take their leave of us.

I was at the back step as the priest

came out. The stars had begun to thicken above our town. I felt his great hand on my shoulder.

'Sometimes there can seem to be no light,' he whispered. 'There can seem no sense in it.'

He squeezed me.

'You must pray very hard, my son.'

When he'd gone Colin moved past me into the deeper darkness of the lawn. I went to stand beside him. Soon Catherine came through the threshold behind us. Our faces reflected the light from the house, and we were silvery like moons. We looked over this small place: the house with Mam and her youngest daughters visible in it, the twins moving across the window with trays of food in their hands, the lights and rooftops of this small town, St Patrick's steeple, the lights of the great city beyond and the sky above.

'Why did he die?' asked Catherine.

No answer, silence, nothing.

The world plunged unstoppably through the wilderness. Ice began to form on our clothes and hair.

I knew from school that we would

journey through a meteor storm that night. We waited, close together, until the first of the falling stars appeared. We gasped and pointed and whispered the numbers, but we lost count as the storm intensified and stars cascaded out of the diminishing night.

BEATING THE BOUNDS

We heard the trumpet as we walked from church towards the Heather Hills. It was Ascension Day. We were nibbling biscuits to break our fast. I had a tin of hard-boiled eggs and bread and butter. Catherine carried the water. Colin had the kettle, the packet of tea, the milk, the mugs, the matches.

Margaret made us pause and listen on Felling Bank. It came from the east, from Springwell way. It was squeaky, tuneless, determined. It came with the subdued ringing of a bell, the screeching of children.

'What is it?' she said.

'Just kids,' said Colin. 'Nothing. Come on. Keep moving.'

We shrugged, and continued walking. It didn't stop.

'How do we know it was Thursday?' said Mary.

We looked at her.

'The priest said it was a day just like today and it was Thursday. How do we know that?'

'It's in the Bible,' said Catherine. 'It was on a Thursday on Mount Olivet. He was attended by angels as he rose. The souls of those who had been in Limbo entered Heaven at his side.'

'Hell's teeth,' said Colin.

'And we can follow them if we're worthy,' said Catherine.

Mary contemplated this, then started giggling.

'Mrs Minto!' she said. 'Mrs Minto!' And we laughed together at the memory: the entranced woman walking to the altar during the elevation of the Host; her moans of ecstasy or pain; the way she'd prostrated herself on the altar steps; Father O'Mahoney getting redder and redder as he tugged her coat and whispered at her to get up; her battered hat and her face all wet and wild as he returned her to her seat. Then her deep sobbing, her jabbered prayers, Maureen McNulty from the Legion of Mary sitting comfortingly at her side.

'Maybe she saw something,' said Margaret.

'Or was touched by the Holy Spirit or something,' said Catherine.

'Like the apostles in that picture,' said Mary. 'The dove and the tongues of fire.'

Colin clicked his tongue.

'That's Pentecost,' he said. 'It hasn't happened yet. Come on. Keep moving.'

We moved through the streets and lanes and past the allotments on Windy Ridge and on to the high playing fields. Margaret said she felt weak, she couldn't wait to eat the eggs and the bread. We were starving: nothing but communion and the biscuits since yesterday.

'How far is it?' she said.

'Won't be long,' said Catherine, taking her hand. 'Don't worry. It won't be long.'

Brilliant light. A few high wispy clouds. A gentle breeze, the scent of grass and wood-smoke. A noise of larks, of dogs barking, of the trumpet, getting louder.

In the Heather Hills we followed a rough track through heather and gorse, past the many caves and excavations

33

made by children. We gathered twigs for the fire as we walked. I ripped brittle branches from a dead hawthorn and snapped them across my thigh. We chose a bank of turf above one of the clay ponds near the crest. We could see westwards into the hills of County Durham, eastwards to the North Sea. Felling sloped away below us: the fields, the rooftops, the steeple, the black river. Nearby were the roofs and tall chimneys of the hospital. Then the city, filling the land to the north.

We made our fire in one of the many rings of stones where earlier fires had been. We rested the kettle full of water in the flames. We cracked the shells of our eggs on stones. We sighed and smiled as we ate.

'They used to build beacons here,' said Cohn. 'Times of disaster and celebration. Could be seen for miles around.'

There were voices now, laughter, children's voices howling and giggling, the trumpet, the bell, and at last the procession appeared, coming through the hills. In front were the town clerk,

Mr Dobbs, in his suit and tie and his chain of office; the Reverend Carr in his tweeds; Miss Fowler the headteacher of Falla Park Junior; the policeman Sergeant Fox; Colonel Gibson from the Salvation Army. Then a straggle of adults and children and yapping dogs behind. The trumpeter was a fat boy in shorts who danced and swayed as he blew. A little girl rang the bell, holding it shyly at her side.

Mary squeaked with laughter, pointed into the little crowd, named the faces she knew.

Mr Dobbs had a map in one hand and a long cane in the other. After a few yards he brought the procession to a halt, flourished the map in the air and beat the earth with the cane.

'This is the boundary!' he called. 'This is the boundary!'

Boys ran from the mob towards him. He chose one, and pretended to beat the boy as severely as he had beaten the earth.

'This is the boundary!' he called again. 'This is the boundary!'

The boy squealed and the procession

laughed. The trumpeter blew more loudly, the girl rang her bell more shyly, they all moved on.

Mr Dobbs saw us and he waved. He spoke to the vicar then waded through the bracken towards us. His plump face was flushed, his golden chain glittered in the sunlight.

'Now then!' he called, hurrying past the pond. 'Now then!' He bent double, breathless and giggling. He held up the map and struck the turf with his stick.

'Know what this lot is?' he said.

We shook our heads and he giggled.

'Beating the bounds,' he said.

He showed the boundary of Felling marked in red on the map.

He said, 'Once upon a time when there were no true maps, we marked the earth to show where one place ended and another place began. We thumped the earth to mark it. We thumped the children to fix it in their brains.' He giggled. 'The children grew up, did their thumping in turn, passed it on from generation to generation. Hard times, eh? How's Mam?'

'In hospital again,' said Margaret.

'Visiting this afternoon,' said Mary.

'She's had some stick, eh?' said Mr Dobbs. He smiled. 'Give her my best.'

He looked at the fire and the steaming kettle and the eggs in our fists.

'Having a wild day, then? That's the style.'

He thumped the turf by our fire, looked back towards the procession, giggled.

'Did it on Ascension Day, on the day Our Lord entered Heaven, to remind ourselves of our earthly state.'

He tousled Margaret's and Mary's hair.

'Thought we'd revive it,' he said. 'A bit of history. A bit of fun.'

He fumbled in his pocket and took a handful of jelly babies out.

'There you are now,' he said, giving them to the girls. 'Go on, get them down.'

The vicar and Miss Fowler were smoking cigarettes. The Colonel was kicking a dog from his heels. Sergeant Fox strolled through the stragglers with his hands clasped behind his back. The trumpeter swayed and the trumpet squealed.

'Now then,' said Mr Dobbs. 'Must get on. Like to join us now?'

'No thank you,' said Colin.

We looked at him but he shook his head.

'Ah, well,' said Mr Dobbs.

He stood there beaming, then turned away.

'Give her my best, now, eh?' he called from past the pond. He waved the procession forward. He peered at the map. He struck the earth.

'This is the boundary! This is the boundary!'

'Why not?' said Mary.

'We can't,' said Colin.

'Why not, though?'

He shrugged.

'Don't know. But there was no priest there, was there?'

We stared after the procession, that was making its way through the rough tracks of the Heather Hills and would soon be out of sight. A few stragglers brought up the rear: a knot of fighting boys, an old man with a Jack Russell on

38

a string, a couple of little girls heaving a great shining pram with a bawling baby over the awkward ground.

'Maybe we're not interested in where we are on earth,' said Colin. 'Maybe on Ascension Day we just think of when we'll be in Heaven.'

We looked at him. He clicked his tongue and lit a cigarette.

'Hell's teeth!' he said. 'Maybe anything. I don't know, do I?'

Catherine put the tea in the mugs and poured boiling water on the tea.

'Perhaps that's it,' she said. 'Like Father O'Mahoney said this morning, this day lifts this world of pain a little closer up to Heaven.'

We waited for our tea to cool. We sprawled on the soft turf. The trumpet quietened. The sun poured down. Margaret asked how long it was until the hospital but there were hours yet.

She sighed.

'She'll be waiting,' she said. 'She'll be so lonely. Her leg'll be so sore. Why does she have to put up with it?'

She lay face down, singing to herself. Mary found a stick and traced the shape of Margaret's body on to the grass.

'This is the boundary,' she said.

We marked the shape with little stones. We stood back and looked at it and Margaret giggled.

We traced each other, marked each of our shapes with stones on the grass. The shapes lay side by side between the fire and the pond.

'There we are,' said Mary. 'A map of us all.'

We laughed and drank our tea and we heard another voice calling:

'This is the boundary! This is the bloody boundary!'

Two boys came towards the crest, a skinny young one and an older one. The older boy had a stick. He held the young one by the arm and pushed him forward. He kept pausing, whipping the young boy, laughing.

'This is the boundary! This is the bloody boundary!'

Mary jumped up and yelled.

'Stop it! Leave him alone!'

The boy stuck his fingers up at us, pushed the young boy forward.

We looked at Colin.

'Hell's teeth,' he said.

He and I went forward past the ponds. I lifted a stone, gripped it tight in my fist. The boy waited, grinning. He jerked the young boy's hand up towards his shoulder-blade. He stuck his fingers up again.

'Leave him alone,' said Colin.

'Nick off.'

'Leave him alone, I said.'

I held the stone high in the air.

'What'll you do about it?'

'He'll beat your brains out,' said Colin.

'Do it!' yelped the young boy. He squealed as his arm was yanked higher. 'Do it! Beat his brains out!' He howled, lost in his pain.

The older boy relaxed his grip as we moved closer.

'Have him,' he said. He pushed the boy, tripped him, sent him tumbling. He landed with his hands stretched out into the clay pond.

'Look at him,' he said. 'What is he, eh?'

The young boy slithered from the

41

pond towards us. 'Beat his brains out,' he said. 'Do it. Go on!'

But we moved backward with him, towards the girls.

The other sneered and walked off, lashing the bracken as he went.

'Who are you?' asked Margaret.

'Valentine Carr,' he whimpered, curling up on the turf beside us.

'And who was he?'

'Big bad blinking brother. Adrian Carr.'

'Don't cry now. He's gone away.'

'Poor Valentine,' said Margaret. She rested her hand on his shoulder. 'Poor little Valentine.'

We watched him, waited for him to settle. He wiped his face with his hands, daubed clay on his cheeks.

'What's he done to you?' said Catherine.

He lifted his shirt and showed the red weals on his back.

She listened to his heart, felt his pulse, stared into his eyes, touched his cheek. She gave him some tea and bread and butter.

'There you are,' she said.

He ate and drank between his sobs.

'Don't worry, Valentine,' she whispered. 'You'll be all right. Valentine. It's a nice name.'

'Was born on St Valentine's Day. She said everybody would love me for it. But everybody picks on me for it. What's your names?'

We told him. We showed him our outlines on the grass. We told him to lie down and we placed the stones around him.

'See?' said Catherine. 'There's us and there's Valentine beside us. See?'

'Yes.'

'Good boy. Sit still. Forget about it all.'

'What time is it?' said Margaret.

'Hours yet,' said Catherine.

We sprawled there in the silence in the heat. In the distance, the trumpet and the bell continued. Soon Valentine was sleeping. Mary and Catherine lay dozing, too. Colin and I smoked cigarettes. Margaret pulled handfuls of clay from the edge of the pond and formed little squat figures with it. She walked them across the grass like

43

puppets. She made wings on some of them and held them up to the sky.

'Put them in the fire,' said Colin. 'They'll harden and you'll be able to take them home.'

We knelt around the fire, gently laying the figures on the embers. I put more hawthorn there and the flames began to crackle and flare around them. We put up our hands, protecting our faces.

'Don't worry,' I said. 'They won't burn.'

'I'll take one for Mam,' said Margaret. 'That one there, look.'

She stared into the flames.

'How long will they take?'

'Long as you can leave them,' said Colin. 'Till they're hot right through and they're baked like bread and they're hard as stone.'

'She'll put it on the bedside table. Every time she looks at it she'll think of us.'

Valentine woke up and came to us.

'Can you take me home now?' he said.

We looked at each other.

'But what time is it?' said Margaret.

'Where do you live?' said Colin.

'I don't know,' said Valentine.

'Hell's teeth, Valentine!'

We took him back to where we could look down over Felling. We pointed out the streets radiating out from Felling Square, the parks, the new flats, the old estates.

'Somewhere down there?' we said.

'I don't know! I don't know!'

Catherine came and named places he might live, the landmarks he might live beside. She stroked his shoulder.

'I don't know,' he whimpered. 'I don't know how to get home again.'

She shook her head and sighed.

'I dreamed about the Ascension,' she said. 'Jesus came out from St Patrick's. He was lifted slowly up into the sky. I kept pointing to him but nobody noticed a thing. He got smaller and smaller and smaller and then he was gone. The sky was very blue and very empty, just like today.'

Valentine leaned on her.

'Take me home, Catherine.'

She clicked her tongue and shook

her head at him.

'Hell's teeth, Valentine. Somebody must have told you where you live. Is it big or small? Is it a flat or a house?'

He stared down at the grass.

'Think about it! Think!'

He thought and cried.

'I think I remember,' he said at last. 'I think it starts with The.'

'Hell's teeth,' said Colin. 'The bloody what?'

'The Hayning?' said Catherine. 'The Crescent? The Green? The Drive?'

His eyes brightened.

'The Drive? Yes? The Drive?'

'I think so. I don't know.'

We looked at each other. We looked over the playing fields and rooftops to the distant curved roadway named The Drive.

'But what time is it?' said Margaret.

Colin looked at his watch: just time enough, if we hurried and Valentine was right.

We gathered our things together. We lifted Margaret's hot figures from the dying embers and laid them in the tin where the eggs and bread had been.

She carried the angel that wouldn't fit, rolling it from hand to hand because of its heat. We hurried out of the Heather Hills and away from the hospital. We kept urging Valentine to move, to hurry, we were doing this for his sake and he should at least try to keep up. He kept stopping, saying he was tired, he was too hot, he wanted to go home, we were being horrible to him. His face was wet and wild and red with weeping. I lost patience with him and half-dragged him across the playing fields.

'Is it near here?' said Catherine as we entered Chilside Road and headed down towards The Drive.

'He doesn't blinking know,' said Mary.

'I think so,' said Valentine. He said yes as we entered The Drive. He wiped his eyes with his fists.

'Yes,' he said. 'That one there.'

We hesitated as he began to lead us towards it.

'Don't leave me yet,' he said, starting to cry again.

We went to the gate. The garden inside was worn smooth as stone.

Someone had been digging a deep hole. A sheet of corrugated steel was thrown across it with Danger Keep Out painted in red. At the side of the house a sleeping mongrel was chained to a clothes post and a fire was smouldering. A man stared from the window, disappeared, appeared at the door. He wore a maroon dressing gown, black boots.

'Who's this?' he said.

They brung me home,' said Valentine. 'My friends.'

'His brother just left him,' said Mary. She pulled up Valentine's shirt. 'And look what he did to him.'

'Get in here,' said the man.

Valentine walked to the door and the man pulled him over the threshold. The door slammed. We heard the yelling from inside.

'Adrian! Get here! Many times have I told you not to leave him? Many times have I told you not to hit the little sod?'

Then there was Adrian's voice, yelling in pain and cursing too, and Valentine looking out at us through his

48

tears.

'Poor little Valentine,' we murmured as he was dragged from our sight.

'We'll see him again,' said Catherine.

'We'll take him to see Mam,' said Mary.

'Yes. Some day. Poor little soul.'

We turned away and Margaret sighed: she was so tired and hot, the way back was so steep. Mam would be so worried if we weren't there on time.

The distant rooftops and chimneys of the hospital shimmered in the heat.

We heard a voice:

'Here they are! Oh, here they are!'

It was Mrs Minto in her garden. She knelt at the border of her lawn with a trowel in her hand. She still had her battered hat on and when she rose and came to the fence we saw the little squares of carpet tied around her knees with string.

'Fancy that!' she called. 'How lovely! How nice to see you all!'

She stood there beaming, with dirt on her face and a ladybird crawling over the front of her green blouse. 'Don't move, now!'

She trotted off to her open back door and came back with a bottle of sarsaparilla in her hand. She passed it across the fence and we drank and handed it on to each other.

'Fancy you lot coming past my fence on such a lovely day. Suppose you're off to see your Mam. Give her my love. Make sure, now.'

She took a packet of biscuits from her pocket and passed them over, too.

'Go on,' she said. 'You need the nourishment. Get them down.'

Colin looked at his watch and said it was all right. We'd be there on time. So we stood there and munched and drank and started to smile.

'So lovely,' said Mrs Minto. 'So warm and bright. Jesus safe in Heaven. Mam tucked up in hospital, and here's us all together on God's good earth.'

Margaret inspected the angel in her hand. The surface was crumbly and one of the wings had snapped.

'Don't worry,' whispered Catherine. 'She'll love it just the same.'

I lifted the lid of the tin and showed the others resting safe in there.

The trumpet and bell sounded from a distant boundary. Mrs Minto tilted her head.

'Can you hear that?' she said. 'It's gone round and round in my head all day long.'

THE BABY

There was a seamstress, Miss Golightly, who lived in Kitchener Street behind Felling Square. We bought our gloves and balaclavas from her. She lengthened our hems and altered our hand-me-downs. She was no taller than I, she smelt of mints and embrocation and cologne. She had a thin moustache and her earlobes were stretched by the silver earrings she wore. On cold days a tatty fur stole with animals' heads hung over her cardigan and stared at you with stupid glassy eyes.

There were kids who said she was a witch and who wouldn't pass her door at night. They talked about spells and spirits. They said she'd stolen children and sold them to the devil. Her great-nephew, Kev, a red-haired boy of my own age, said the stories were true. He hated her. He said his family knew she'd done terrible things. She'd been a whore in her youth and after that nobody'd touch her with a barge-pole and that was why she was alone.

'Watch yourself,' he used to say. 'She's a filthy cow. She'll start touching you up. Just you wait and see.'

When I repeated some of this at home, Mam said there wasn't a harmful bone in the woman's body. She wanted no more than to have children to make and mend for, and she loved us all. This seemed true to me. I liked to be with her in her little front room, to stand on a chair before her while she held her pins between her teeth and tugged at hems and seams. She touched me so gently as she smoothed the clothes to fit the body. She stroked my hair and said how quickly I grew. Afterwards there were jars of wrapped sweets on her sideboard, dozens of books on her shelves, framed faded photographs on her walls.

The photographs seemed alien and ancient at first, but she guided me to see that the unknown existed within the familiar: that carnival with its brass band and tents and roundabouts took place on the fields at Felling Shore;

those horses with the great leather halters around their necks drank from a trough at the centre of Felling Square; that steep row of shops with the aproned proprietors outside was Felling High Street. Everywhere, there were glimpses of the world in which I'd grown: the broad river, the curve of the Heather Hills, St Patrick's steeple, the unmistakeable gradients and intersections of our streets, the shapes of buildings beneath reconstructed facades, the names of public houses and businesses rewritten but unchanged. I sought familiarity in the people, too, looking for my ancestry in the faces of those who had been dead still while the film was exposed, and trying to decipher the shapes of those who had moved and left only translucent impressions like ghosts.

As I leaned close, I kept whispering, 'Yes. I see.' And she smiled and nodded and squeezed my arm in congratulation.

There were many pictures of nurses. They posed in formation in hospital grounds, they were busy in field hospitals preparing for the first war. They cared for the casualties: young men on benches or slumped in bathchairs, with their bandages, their stump limbs, their brave smiling, their deadened eyes. Once she brought a parcel from another room: her old uniform, folded and pressed, wrapped in tissue and brown paper; the dark blue skirts and the brilliant white pinafore, the cross on the bib darkened to the colour of blood. She held it before her body and posed for me. She directed me to the photographs. 'Where am I?' she asked, and time after time I scanned the faces until I learned to see her quick and true: the little bright and beaming one, who still survived in the gentle seamstress at my side.

*   *   *

It was inevitable that as I grew older her seams should begin to pucker and twist. We noticed it first when she was making me trousers from a length of blackout we'd found in the back of a

55

drawer. She was distracted that day, she found it difficult to focus on her task.

'How old are you?' she asked.

'Ten,' I answered.

She counted on her fingers, whispered numbers, decades. 'Ten?'

'Yes. Ten.'

'Ten.'

She meditated, or dreamed, with her needle poised in mid-air. It was November, near to Remembrance Day. I remember the red poppies we were wearing at our breasts. Frost was resting in the joints of the cobbles outside. A family hurried by, parents and small children in a close group with their breath in clouds around them. When she came out of it and stitched again, her fingers slipped and she drew a little bulb of blood from my leg.

'Poor soul,' she whispered as she dabbed my skin with cotton wool. 'Such tender things.'

She stitched again, half-dreaming.

'How old are you?' she asked. 'How old?'

Afterwards we stood before the photographs again.

'There you are,' I told her.

'And here's this one,' she said.

Beneath her finger was a grinning black-haired soldier, helmet in his hand, thick uniform buttoned to his throat. He stood by a front door like hers, that opened directly to the pavement. Even in this darkened print you saw how the sun had beaten down that day, glared upon the brick walls and the threshold, how the soldier narrowed his dark eyes against the relentless light and grinned and grinned.

'See?' she said.

'Yes.'

She turned me to another photograph, a crowd of soldiers in loose formation on a railway platform on a duller day.

'Where is he?' she said.

I played the game, scanned the faces.

'That one.'

'No. This one,' she said. 'This bonny one.'

We went to other photographs.

'Where is he?'

'This one.'

'No, this one. See?'

'I see.'

She cupped my chin in her palm. She pressed my cheek with the tips of her cold fingers, pressed harder upon my cheekbone, traced the delicate curve of my temple.

'Silly bonny boy,' she said. 'And where is he now?'

She dreamed again, then left me and went to somewhere else in the house and came back with another photograph. It was the head of the soldier, in shirt and tie, relaxed, hardly faded at all, smiling through the even light at us. The name of a Felling photographer was embossed in the corner of the print.

'Here he is,' she said.

She touched the flesh of my cheek again.

She wrapped up the trousers in brown paper.

'I told him, you know. Don't go. Nurses know the body's such a soft and fragile thing.'

At home, Mam fingered the crooked stitching at my waist. She tugged the material and tried to make it fall evenly to my ankles. She knelt at my side with scissors and needle and thread, opened the stitches, tried to close them again more evenly. She sighed and shook her head and said they'd just have to do, I could use them for playing in.

I told her about the soldier.

'Poor body,' she whispered. 'Poor soul.'

We didn't use Miss Golightly for some time afterwards. Mam still called on her, and came back with stories of how she was failing.

*   *   *

It was my eleven-plus year. Dad said that I was carrying the dreams of the past, that I was a pioneer. Preparation at school was relentless: day after day of Maths Progress Tests and English Progress Tests and prayers that the hardworking would be rewarded. I took the examination at Jarrow Grammar School. There were scores of us there, ranked and registered in the yard by district and school and name. BAN THE BOMB and great CND symbols were painted on the corrugated roofs of the outside classrooms. Stern teachers stood around us like warders. Even in the toilets we were watched. I stood dazed in there, stared at myself in a cracked mirror, saw the baby and the boy in me, saw the images of my parents upon me. Someone yelled at me to move, to get out. As I stumbled past him he shoved me on my way.

When I began to write in the regimented hall, in a silence broken by scared breathing and the padding feet of invigilators, I began to be released. I knew, as Dad had said, there was nothing for me to worry about, that I would be rewarded.

I passed, and the uniform was grey: grey flannel blazer with a badge of battlements and lances, grey flannel cap, grey shorts and socks. The blazer slopped down over my shoulders, the shorts kept slipping down across my hips. I stood at the centre of the family and they smiled and giggled. Dad put his arm around me and said who knew what wonders time would bring. He took me around the town in his Austin. He burst in on our relatives and called down their congratulations upon me. They laughed at my shyness and pressed coins in my hand. They poured glasses of beer for Dad. His own father told me he'd seen it in me as soon as I was born.

Dad took me to Miss Golightly to have tucks sewn into the shorts. He left me there and walked around the corner to the Columba Club. She beamed with joy, kissed my cheek, said she'd thought I'd left her.

She stood me before her and tugged my uniform into place.

She wore a battered cardigan. The flesh on her cheeks was sagging and wrinkled. There was a vague scent of urine in the house. When she began to tack my shorts with pins she trembled. When I felt her fingers on my skin, I thought of what Kev had said and I cursed myself for it. I sat with a towel around me while she held the shorts in her hands and worked with needle and thread. Spring light poured in from the street, fragments of silvery dust were buoyed upon it. I gazed around the little crowded room, at the photographs.

'Miss Golightly,' I said. 'What happened to the soldier?'

She looked at me in surprise. I could see how her eyes strained to focus on me after staring at the needle point. She clicked her tongue, raised her eyebrows, laughed a little.

'Death,' she said. She went back to her work. 'That's all. Just death.'

I put the shorts back on. I stood before her. She touched my cheek.

'How old now?' she asked.

'Eleven.'

We unwrapped sweets together and stood before the photographs.

'My bonny boy,' she whispered.

She sighed. She squeezed my arm. I felt how small beside me she had become.

'You'll be going off soon,' she said.

She dreamed.

'This is secret,' she whispered.

She left me. I heard her footsteps on the stairs. She came back with a polished wooden box in her hands. She put it on the sideboard, lifted its lid with trembling hands, then took the jar out from inside and showed her baby to me.

It was a foetus suspended in liquid. It was hardly longer than my thumb. There were buds of eyes and nose and mouth on its face, little half-formed hands raised to the chest, little knees raised to the belly. It rested upright with its spine gently arched as it curled in upon itself.

'My little boy,' she whispered.

She rested her palm upon the curve of the jar.

'He would have been like you are.'

We watched the baby in the liquid, the thin shaft of light falling upon him.

'What's he called?' I asked.

'He would have been Anthony, like his father. But death happened in me too.'

She put her arm across my shoulder. We were silent and we dreamed.

'Do you see us in him?' she asked.

'Me and my soldier?'

Then Dad was knocking on the door. She put the jar back in the box. She kissed me and told me it was secret. When she let Dad in she told him what a fine lad I'd become. He laughed, and said hadn't he just come from showing off about me in the Columba Club.

*   *   *

I grew quickly that summer. I played in the blackout trousers. They faded, they tightened, the hems frayed and holes were worn into the knees. I played in the great football games on the high playing fields: dozens of boys from opposing streets rushing at the ball and kicking and cursing each other. I set off with my friends on expeditions into the Heather Hills. We carried knives and homemade spears and parcels of sandwiches. We looked down upon the new buildings, rising in Felling Square. We squatted among the ruins of the old gun-site, peered to the distant North Sea, reported bombers coming in. We lit fires and smoked cigarettes pinched from our fathers. Our bodies ached and tingled with sunlight, exhaustion, exhilaration. We lay close together in the warm long grass and talked of the journeys we'd take when we'd grown.

Sometimes I came across Kev Golightly. He grinned at me and talked of the filthy old witch and asked if she'd been in my pants yet.

I dreamt of Miss Golightly's slackening flesh, of her dead soldier, of her baby in the jar. Often it began to grow, familiar features to appear in its face.

Late August I went with Dad to buy new pens and a mathematics set. I put on the uniform again, felt how the blazer had become a closer fit. A bus pass naming my route was sent to me. The days were shortening fast. Earlier and earlier we looked down from the hills to the whole of Tyneside fading into the dusk.

'That's it,' we whispered on the final evening as we went back down.

*   *   *

Miss Golightly's heart gave out that October. A child who passed through Kitchener Street one morning saw her lying dead at the centre of her living-room. I went with my parents to the funeral. She lay in her coffin at the front of the church while the service was said. I knew that she would have already begun to decay and I tried to imagine her lying in there. I wore my uniform, and I fingered the last stitches she'd made for me, which would soon need to be undone. We spoke the prayers and sang the hymns for her. The minister said that she had left the troubled body behind and had been born again into glory. I said a private prayer that her soldier would be waiting for her. I heard her voice in me: Where am I? Where is he? and I cried, for I understood that their baby could not be there with her.

Afterwards, as we drove home in the Austin, Mani said she'd heard Miss Golightly's family had been awful, already fighting to get their hands on the few things she'd owned.

By then I'd heard teachers whispering that I was the best of my year. Dad said I had the world in the palm of my hand. Mam smiled as she unpicked Miss Golightly's stitches, and asked where her little boy had gone. One evening Kev Golightly's mother came to the door with a parcel. She said the old woman had written a note that I should have these. She scowled and told Mam it would take weeks to get rid of the clutter. She said you wouldn't believe the things they'd found in there. She stood and watched as I unwrapped the photographs of the nurses and soldiers and of Felling as it was. She looked at Mann and raised her eyes and shook her head and hurried out into the night. Dad helped me to put the photographs up in my bedroom. I showed them Miss Golightly in her youth. I showed them her soldier. Together we picked out the familiar features of our town. I recalled Miss Golightly's brightness, her gentle touch.

In the evenings I sat beneath the photographs to work out my problems and write my compositions. I tried once to write the story of a nurse, a soldier, a baby in a jar, but it came to nothing. I knew I wouldn't get away with it.

Autumn deepened, darkened. Frost came early. On Saturday mornings the football games on the high playing fields continued. Their ferocity was intensified by the cold and there were often bitter running battles on the sidelines. Below us smoke thickened in the still air over the town. White frost lay in the shadows. In the Heather Hills we lit fires and dropped potatoes into the embers. We wrenched thick sheets of ice from the ponds. We talked of girls and the bomb. We imagined that we were survivors after war, that waste and death were all around us.

It was on a Saturday afternoon that I came upon Kev again. I was making my way home. I heard him calling my name, saw him coming towards me across the fields.

'You won't believe it,' he said.

He took a haversack from his

shoulder, took out the polished wooden box from inside.

'You've seen nothing like it,' he said.

He opened the box and took out the jar and held it towards me.

'Look,' he said.

I took it from him and held it to the fading light. I saw the half-formed features, the little legs, the little arms.

'There was a note that it should be buried with her. Nobody'd touch it, though. My mam cried all night about it. My dad wouldn't go near it. Said it was evil. Everybody thinks somebody else took it away.' He leaned close to me. 'See?' he said. 'They were right about the cow. A bloody witch.'

The baby turned gently in the liquid as I moved it against the light.

'You think it's real?' he whispered.

The baby's flesh through the years had become darker, more opaque than ours, but I saw the outlines of bones and blood vessels. The outline of his skin was blurred, as if he had started to dissolve. He held up his hands as if to hold on to or fend off something.

'He'll be in Limbo,' I said.

He looked at me.

'Where the souls of the unchristened go. You can be happy there. But you can't know God, and you can't be with the christened.'

He grinned.

'It's even got a dick. If you tip it up you'll see it.'

'What you doing with it?' I asked.

He shrugged.

'Don't know. I was going to get it out. I got the lid off, then I didn't dare.'

We stared at each other. He took the jar from me and started to unscrew the metal lid. We breathed deeply. There was a chemical scent as the lid came off.

'I thought of you,' he said. 'Soon as I got it.'

We sighed and bit our lips. We watched his fingers reaching in. He grunted and recoiled, couldn't do it. Some of the liquid slopped out on to the grass.

'Stupid,' I said.

I looked at the sky, the disappearing sunlight. I told Kev to clear off. I said I'd take the baby. We fought, rolling over on the frosty grass, but I was bigger than him and it was soon over. I held him by the throat and said he knew nothing about this. I said it was secret and I'd kill him if he told. I grinned and said there were spells she'd taught me. I grunted some mumbo-jumbo and spat down on to the grass beside his face.

'Stupid sod,' I said.

I let him up. I threw the haversack at him. There were tears and blood on his face. I stepped towards him and he backed away. I put the lid back on the jar and the jar back in the box.

'Go on,' I told him.

I took my knife from my pocket and folded out its blade. He lurched away across the field. He kept cursing me, sobbing. I watched him, waited till he'd gone.

I moved back up into the Heather Hills. The light was fading fast. I broke the ice on a pond. I found a sheltered grassy spot close by, beneath a hawthorn tree. I started to dig with the knife. After the icy crust the earth crumbled easily and I scooped it out with my fingers. I poured the liquid out of the jar, holding the baby back with the lid. I tore a strip of blackout from my trousers, laid it across my hand. I took the lid away and the baby tumbled out on to my palm. I reached into the pond, lifted some water, trickled it over the baby.

'I name you Anthony,' I said.

I prayed that the Devil would be defeated, that the baby would be acceptable to God, that he would be welcomed now. I stared down at him, touched him, his skin so smooth, so tender. I folded the cloth over him.

'There you are,' I whispered and placed him in the earth.

I pushed the soil back and pressed the turf back into place and prayed again that my deeds on Earth might influence events in Heaven. I threw the jar and the box into the wilderness.

I hurried back down through the dusk.

In my room, I put my schoolwork aside. I still felt the weight and shape of the baby on my skin. As it faded, I began again to write the story of the nurse, the soldier and the baby in the jar.

THE ANGEL OF CHILSIDE ROAD

This road is narrow and tall trees grow from its verges. It leads upwards from Heworth and Watermill Lane. It comes to a broad sloping field which in those days led to the colliery and then the Heather Hills and then the open sky.

The week after our sister Barbara died she was seen walking hand-in-hand with Mam on this road towards the field. She was dressed in white and both she and Mam walked with a fluency which neither had in their lives, for Barbara had been an invalid child and Mam was already badly damaged by arthritis. It was late winter. They were beneath the trees. A light was burning from our sister and both of them were smiling.

At that time we lived at the dark foot of Felling in a new estate of grey pebble-dashed houses, called The Grange. We had moved there from our parents' first home in Felling Square, a cold upstairs flat overrun with mice, which had been condemned. Our house was in a cul-de-sac, Thirlmere, which was entered from a long looped road called Coniston. This estate was separated from the body of the town by the new bypass. From the garden at Thirlmere it was possible to stand on tiptoe and peer over the rooftops to the distant centre of the town, the streets and parks, the playing fields, the Heather Hills, but there was no easy access to those places. It was in the house at Thirlmere that Barbara died.

After she died, we soon began to move upwards again. We returned to Felling Square, to the new flats that replaced those that had been demolished. Then higher, to Coldwell Park, where we stayed, close to Chilside Road. If our father had not died, it's probable we would have ascended again, perhaps to the new estates built beyond the fields once the colliery had gone.

Perhaps in our dreams we will always move closer to the sky, following the angel that was seen on Chilside Road that day.

The angel was seen by Mary Byrne, mother of Michael, and resident of Watermill Lane. She gave her account to our mother, to whom it brought much comfort, who told our sister Catherine, who told it to us all.

THE TIME MACHINE

Felling Shore, early May, the year before my father dies. The first time I've nested in years. I'm in an ancient hawthorn, with a hedge-sparrow's egg in my mouth. I hear birdsong, the endless din of the distant city, then a grinding of gears and engines, the crunch of wheels on damaged roads. I step higher on to a thin bough, and pull aside the tangled leaves. I see caravans and lorries coming down through the terraced streets, mounting the broken kerbs on to the waste ground, entering this broad field above the Tyne. The tree that holds me quivers as I grip it tighter. Its thorns pierce my skin. I see the Waltzer and the House of Death. A sheep, a goat and a little camel lie in the same cage. I slip, the egg burst on my tongue. I gag and spit. Salt and slime in my mouth. The shell ineffably fine. The ruined egg dangles from my lips. I grip a new branch, re-balance, stare out again. Through the hawthorn blossom I see the Time Machine return to Felling Shore.

I climb down, squat in the shade of the tree. The convoy comes to rest. Children and dogs leap from its doors to the field. I spit and spit, wipe my mouth with my sleeve. Blood trickles from my hands. A group of the children come. A little girl in a short frock with an Alsatian at her side points at me, then at the old shoebox at my side.

'What's in there?' she says.

I open the box, show the eggs laid in neat rows on smooth sand. I touch them with my fingers, and name them.

'Starling, larky, blackbird, wren.'

I point up into the tree, to the nest deep in the foliage.

'Hedge-sparrow,' I tell her.

I pick a fragment of shell from the tip of my tongue.

'Give us an egg,' she says.

I hold out the bright blue fragment to her.

She laughs, grips the growling dog by its mane. Beyond her, men are already uncoupling trailers, throwing rods and girders down on to the grass, unrolling great sheets of canvas. I see the Time Machine, sky blue, with pyramids and flying saucers and fleshy pink women in bathing costumes painted on it, at the centre the arched entrance with its beaded curtain.

A skinny naked boy crouches before the eggs, shoves his finger into the sand. I clip his hand away.

'Which one you from?' I ask the girl.

'We tell your age for sixpence. Dad gets out of chains and sticks skewers in himself. Mam tells your fortune and shows her knickers to men after midnight.' She held her hand out. 'Give us a penny, eh?'

'What's your name?'

'Little Kitten.' She shows her nails like claws. 'You're fourteen. Give us a penny.'

I drop a coin in her palm and she giggles and spits then sets off to the river with the dog and her friends. Out in the field, older children are roaming now. A juggler spins knives. Elvis Presley's voice starts to crackle and roar. I move out from the tree. The woman leaning against the Time Machine hails me as I walk by. She is blonde, plump like the women in the paintings. I see how the name and the bodies have been painted time and again.

'Yes you, boy!' she calls.

She wears high heels, short skirt. Make-up is caked on her face, her eyes are rimmed by black mascara. I start to turn away, then catch my breath at the tenderness I see in her. She is thirty, or older, or even my mother's age. She smiles, she licks her lips, she tugs gently at the straps beneath her white blouse. I stare at the entrance to the Time Machine, at the darkness inside.

'Make sure you come and see the Time Machine,' she says. I stare at her.

'Remember,' she whispers. 'Remember, bonny boy.' I turn my eyes away, I leave the field, I hurry home.

*   *   *

I'm in the kitchen with my sisters. Dust seethes in the sunlight that's pouring in. Light flares in the loose strands

80

of my sisters' hair. We gaze at the eggs. We practise naming them, remembering them.

'Blackbird,' we whisper. 'Starling, larky, wren.'

I show them the paired pinholes in each egg, tell them how to blow out the stuff from inside. I tell them it was Dad who taught me all this, who years ago took Colin and me through the old lanes at Felling's edges. I tell them the rules he taught me: be silent and quick, don't damage the nest, take only one egg, and only when the clutch is three or more.

I see tears in Catherine's eyes.

'What's wrong?' I say. 'What's wrong?'

She raises her hand into the streaming light. We watch the dust in silvery fragments dance and seethe about us.

'Human skin,' she says. 'They told us at school— the majority of dust is human skin. Dead skin.'

We meditate upon this. We laugh. The dust rises and falls, we watch it stream into our mouths with breath.

'Angels are like this,' says Catherine. 'Their bodies are subtler than ours. Their atoms are dispersed. They are more spirit than matter. They are all around us.'

We look at her.

'They told us at school,' she says. 'It's true.'

We all laugh again.

'It's true,' say Mary and Margaret together. 'It's very very true.'

'It is,' I say. 'And I saw a Time Machine today.'

Dad comes in from the sunlight. He has his heavy herringbone coat over his arm. He kisses the girls and sits with us and sighs at the beauty of the day. He lights a Player's and the smoke weaves and spirals through the dust. He shifts on the hard kitchen chair, catches his breath.

'Press there,' he says, taking my hand, holding it against the base of his spine. I press, feel the complicated solid bone beneath the flesh and skin.

'There?' I ask.

'There. Yes, there. Press harder, son.'

He touches the eggs gently and tells us he's seen a Time Machine today.

'I know,' I say. 'I saw it come to Felling Shore.'

He breathes the smoke from his nostrils.

'I saw it going down,' he says. 'Just as it did those years ago.' He reaches out and touches my cheek.

'Who'd believe it? It's the same Time Machine that I saw on Felling Shore when I was a boy.'

We lean close together, above the eggs.

'You'll have to take me,' he says. 'It won't stay long. You'll have to show me.'

He laughs, touches us all, kisses us all.

He ponders.

'Larky?' he says. 'Blackbird, starling and wren?'

*   *   *

I dream that God clambers through the hawthorn at Felling Shore. He balances on thin boughs, gazes into the nests,

83

carefully takes eggs from clutches of more than three. He holds them on His tongue for a moment then swallows them. Little Kitten watches Him from the ground. She keeps saying, 'Give us an egg, sir. Please give us an egg.' At last He tosses one down to her. It cracks open on her palm as she catches it. A feathered child comes out, bright and tiny as a humming-bird.

I catch my breath. It's our dead sister, Barbara, the fourth of us. I watch her fluttering towards the blue sky and deserts of the Time Machine. 'Forgive us,' whispers Little Kitten. 'Give us another egg, sir.' But God is furious. He glares darkly down at the girl. He becomes careless and clumsy. He shoves egg after egg into His mouth. Yellow yolk and bright blue shell dribble from His lips. The hedges tremble and the air is filled with the alarm cries of parent birds. I see Barbara flutter through the beaded curtain of the Time Machine. I rush to follow her, and wake in the darkness inside.

*　　　*　　　*

Next afternoon Dad calls me from the garden. He's tying the sterns of roses against the fence. He squeezes a bud and we see the petals packed moist and dense inside. He tells me how fortunate I am. He tells me there will be nothing I can't do.

'You understand, don't you?' he says.

I nod.

He smiles, ironic, blows smoke on the aphids to make them die.

'We'll go now,' he says. 'Just you and me, the two of us. I'll take the others later.'

In the house the girls and Mam are at the kitchen table. Colin is somewhere upstairs, trying on his best yellow shirt or his best blue jeans.

Dad takes me inside, brushes my hair down, tugs at my sleeves and hems to make me neat. He lays his herringbone coat across his arm. He sighs, presses his hand into the small of his back.

'Where you two off to?' says Mam.

He grins and winks. 'Nesting,' he

85

says. He kisses the girls. 'I'll take you to the fair later,' he says. 'I won't forget.'

We step out into the streaming light.

'Goodbye, little chicks,' he calls.

*   *   *

An untidy cluster of tents and stalls, a couple of roundabouts turning. The caravans are parked above the water. The din of compressors, Elvis' howl, the scent of onions and boiling fat. The people of Felling move at ease through the field and through the fair. We pause by the hawthorn at the edge of the field. Brilliant light pours down, carries the singing of larks from somewhere high above. Dad faces me, watches me. I see the darkness of his beard beneath his dark skin, the heavy eyebrows, the glittering eyes. I see that soon I will be taller than him.

'Are you happy?' he asks.

I shade my eyes and look away and don't know what to say.

'Not a fair question,' he says. He raises his hand to some passers-by. 'You will be happy. You'll have

86

everything we've missed.'

We move forward. He lights a Player's. We weave our way through the crowds between the shooting galleries and roundabouts. I feel his hand guiding me forward. Little Kitten stands in the walkway wearing a white dress, calling out that she can tell the age of anyone for sixpence. She catches my arm as we pass. She points to Dad. 'Forty-two,' she tells him. She holds out her hand. 'Give us me sixpence, then.' He laughs and tosses the coin to her.

She winks at me.

'Give us an egg,' she squeaks.

We move on.

'It's unbelievable,' he says. 'It's the same Time Machine as in my day. The same woman, the same man. They can't be.'

The woman stands on a low stage before the facade. She wears net tights, a bathing costume whose stiff bodice shimmers like a kingfisher's wing. There is an older man beside her, in black top hat and tails. The beaded curtain is pulled back to expose a cool blue interior. The man leans out towards the gathering crowd. He scans our faces.

'Who is bold enough to enter the Time Machine?' he calls. The woman smiles, so gentle.

'Who could cope with the journey?' she asks. 'Who could understand what will be seen?'

I gaze up at her. Dad's hand rests in the small of my back, pushing me forward. She catches my eye, her gaze moves on. The man holds a glittering black rock to us.

He tells us, 'Here is a stone brought back from the Moon.' He holds a curved piece of brass.

'The breastplate of a centurion,' he calls.

He shows a framed indecipherable script.

'Writing from the ninth millennium,' he whispers.

He leans closer.

'What will the next voyager bring back? What wonder will be added to our marvellous museum?'

She catches my eye again. She leans to me.

'Who will travel with Corinna in the Time Machine?'

There is laughter in the crowd. Some kid calls, 'Me! Me!' Dad's hand stretches across my back. 'You,' he whispers. 'You!'

Corinna grins, leans down again.

'You?' she asks. 'This bonny boy?'

She reaches down for me. I find my hand in her own. I find myself stepping upward. I hear Dad behind me laughing and calling: 'Remember me!'

They hold me between them on the stage. The man grips my shoulders, runs his hands over my arms and hips. 'Call me Morlock,' he tells me. He peers deep into my eyes. He asks my name, my school and I answer softly while Corinna holds my hand and tells me to be brave.

'Are you intelligent?' he asks. 'Can you remember what has been shown to you?'

I nod. My head is reeling. I hear laughter and mockery from the crowd. I see the open curtain of the Time Machine.

'What are your ambitions?' says

Morlock.

I gulp, reel.

'To be happy,' I say.

'Happy! Then what are your dreams?' he says. 'What are your visions? What wonders have come in your young life?'

I stare down at Dad. His eyes burn, they urge me to reply.

Corinna strokes my cheek.

'Be brave,' she whispers.

I see Little Kitten laughing at me from between the stalls. A huge man bound in *heavy* chains lumbers through the field outside.

'What are your dreams?' says Morlock.

'I see God,' I whisper. 'I see babies flying. I go to Heaven and Hell. I see the dead come back to life.'

Morlock laughs. He slaps my back, shakes my hand.

'We have chosen well, Corinna. Take him inside and make the preparations.'

She turns me towards the entrance.

'Who else will come inside?' calls Morlock. 'Who will see our voyager set off on his journey through the ages?

Who will enter our marvellous museum and learn of the intrepid voyagers from the past? Who will be there when the boy returns with his stories and his souvenirs . . . ?'

We enter the blue interior, and behind us the people of Felling begin to step up to pay and follow . . .

*   *   *

Inside: a translucent canopy, straw spread upon the grass, shelves, caskets and cupboards, another low stage, and the machine itself. It's an upright cylinder, tall and broad as a hawthorn tree, made of timber, heavily-varnished. Lights fixed in vertical rows, purple and red, flash on and off, on and off. There's a large dial like a barometer, *The Past* to the left, *The Future* to the right. There's a curved door with heavy brass fittings. Its name is printed in flaking gold paint: *The Time Machine.*

I imagine that I will have to disintegrate, that I will be broken up in there, that my atoms will be dispersed so that I can slip subtly through space and time. I tremble at the thought of this. Corinna puts her arm around my shoulder. I smell her perfume and her sweat. I feel the harsh fibre of her bodice, then above this the soft flesh of her shoulders and breasts. She cups my chin in her palm and kisses me gently on the cheek and asks me to say my name.

'We choose our travellers for their looks and their brains and the wanderlust we see in their eyes,' she whispers. 'I'll be with you. I'll tell you what you must do and what you must say.'

She kisses me again.

'Everything will be fine. Wherever we take you, it will be fine.'

She presses her finger to my lips as Morlock leads the audience in.

They gather before us, they grin. Dad laughs from the back of the crowd. Morlock stands beside me again and tells the crowd he can feel the strength in me.

'The future or the past?' he asks me.

I catch Dad's eye again.

'The future,' I say.

He pulls a lever in the stage and the machine begins to turn and rumble on castors set into the stage. The lights flash more urgently. He hauls the lever back and slowly the machine halts. He stares into my eyes. He says that he can feel my readiness for astounding flight. He presses a button beside the dial.

'Take him in, Corinna,' he says. 'Lead him to the future.'

She leads me to the threshold.

Morlock shakes my hand, kisses Corinna, turns to the crowd again.

'While this boy travels through the ages, I will take you on a tour of our museum. Take him in, Corinna.'

She opens the door, guides me inside. I look back to see the crowd gazing intently after us, Dad waving. The door slides shut, the outer wall begins to turn. Corinna giggles.

'In here,' she says, opening another door, pushing me gently in.

A small square room, a still and peaceful place. Yellow padding on the walls, a padded bench, a shelf of books. Names and dates scratched and carved in the timber door and on the timber between the padding. Blue light filters down through frosted glass in the ceiling. We sit side by side on the bench. Our thighs touch each other's, our outstretched feet touch the opposite walls. I brace myself, hear the rumbling of the outer shell as it plunges through the ages.

'When we return,' says Corinna, 'Mr Morlock and the crowd will ask you some questions. You'll want to know the answers, won't you?'

She reaches up to the shelf above our heads and brings down a folder with *The Shape Of Things To Come* written on its cover. She spreads it over our linked knees, begins to turn its pages. Inside are photographs and drawings and film stills. There are rockets and flying saucers and groups of gentle citizens strolling beneath trees. I see how Corinna's nails are bitten to the quick. The flesh of her thighs swells at each of the thousand holes in her fishnet tights. She puts her arm around me, she speaks to me gently.

'You must say that we found ourselves in a great city. There were buildings all around us that touched the sky. The people wore silken robes and travelled in tiny flying machines. You must say that in the future we will travel to the stars in the blinking of an eye. Machines will do our chores. Disease will be conquered. The savagery of our natures will be tamed and there will be no war. We will begin to communicate telepathically. We will begin to understand how we may make true contact with the dead. All of us will travel easily through time.'

She cups my chin in her palm.

'Yes,' she says. 'We chose well. Listen. This is also what you must say.'

I gaze into her eyes. I listen, and am disappointed by these bland and unsurprising visions. I think of Dad outside. I think of my sister mingling with the earth. I think of dust and angels and of the salty slime that can become a flying thing. I feel her leg against my leg. I turn my eyes from her. I seek the image of a humming-bird, and read the names carved into the machine's heavy timber. They form an intricate deep pattern of letters and numbers. The most recently carved are readable. Those beneath are blurred. Those from the distant past have been written over many times. They are clues, fragments, meaningless cuts in the grain.

Corinna touches my cheek.

'Yes,' she tells me. 'You can add your name.'

With the tip of the knife she gives me I write myself alongside these unknown others. I name myself, I name the place in which I name myself, I name the year in which I name myself. I finger the lettering, trace the outlines of my oblivion. Corinna draws me to her once more.

'This is yours,' she says.

There is money in her palm. She draws me closer. She kisses me on the lips. She presses the coins into my palm.

'Yes, this is yours. I know you'll answer well, so this is yours.'

She touches my cheek, my lips.

'Keep our secret and you could come

to visit me at night.' She smiles. My face rests on her shoulder. I look into the shadow between her breasts.

'It's true,' she whispers. 'You could come to see me.' She laughs. 'Would you like that?'

I nod. I bite my lips. I inhale her perfume, her sweat. I hear her heart beating as the Time Machine rumbles on.

'Everything will be fine,' she whispers. 'Keep our secret, answer the questions. Let me test you. Where did we go to? What did we see?'

I answer well. She grins and applauds.

'What will be defeated?' she whispers.

'Death,' I say.

I lie there for an age with my cheek upon her breast. She whispers that I am a brave one, a perfect time traveller. I almost sleep. I start to dream of my father breaking into fragments, travelling to the future alongside me. Then Corinna shows me a little glass jar, filled with earth. I lift the lid, rub the earth between my fingers, feel the dry grit, the fine dust, nothing growing there.

Our little souvenir,' she says. 'Earth from the far future.' Soon the Time Machine begins to slow, returning us to Felling Shore, early May, the year before my father dies . . .

*   *   *

Dad laughs as we stand there, Corinna and Morlock and I, before the little crowd beneath the blue canopy. We show the jar of earth, we allow the spectators to dip their fingers into it. My head reels at the questions that are called to us. With Morlock's and Corinna's help, I answer. We came to a great city. There was work for everyone, though many days were spent in leisure. The planets seemed as close as countries do now. We understood the nature of God and we saw how his spirit shines in everything. Yes, each of us will be able to travel through time. Yes, we will indeed be happier then. At last, Morlock puts his arm around me. He says the boy is exhausted. He announces that it is over. He tells the crowd that they have seen a wondrous thing and that they may go now. They leave, whispering, wondering, laughing. Dad waits and we step down from the stage.

'I travelled in the Time Machine as a boy,' he says.

Morlock smiles.

'Ah! In my father's day. In Corinna's mother's day.'

Corinna kisses me. She whispers. 'Don't forget. Make sure you come to me.'

Morlock carries the earth to the museum. Corinna waits for us to leave.

We go out and the day is already darkening.

Outside another tent, a woman has many veils draped upon her. She holds open a curtain to inner darkness, a sign above her promises Salome's legendary dance.

Little Kitten squeals at us: 'Forty-two! Forty-two!'

Dad asks, 'Did you see my name in there?'

I search my memory, try to see again

the great mass of names and places and dates.

He laughs, nudges me, breathes smoke into the air.

'It was in there, that's the main thing, even if it's unreadable now.'

I see many watching me, the boy who travelled in the Time Machine.

Outside, there is the man wrapped in chains with a hatful of money before him on the grass. He struggles and squirms before his little crowd.

Beneath the hawthorn we look up towards the cheeping chicks and I recall the shape of God.

Dad watches me and grins as we walk on.

'You enjoyed that, then?'

He laughs.

'Keep the secret, eh? Don't forget.'

*   *   *

Next morning Dad takes the girls to Felling Shore. I linger at home. I rearrange the eggs in my shoeboxes. I open the boxes of eggs that Dad has kept since his own youth. I match the eggs of the past with the eggs of the present: starling with starling, blackbird with blackbird, larky with larky, wren with wren. I can find no differences between them. My mother watches me and asks about my sadness. The light pours down upon us. I want to ask her about the loss of one who was formed in her own body. I want to ask her about the emptiness and angels that are all around us. I want to ask her why eggs are taken from clutches of more than three.

We gaze at each other through the brilliant seething dust. She touches my cheek and smiles. We do not know that this is the year before my father dies.

They return mid-afternoon. They laugh about the House of Death with its ghosts and bats, the little camel that they rode across the shore on. They shudder at the man who pushed skewers through his cheeks. They say that Little Kitten knows the ages of us all. We nibble coconut flesh and sip its milk. Colin sits with us in his yellow shirt. He tells us that last night he rode the Waltzer far into the dark. He taps a fast rhythm on the table, recalling a frantic song.

Later I lie in the garden, in the glare. Dad works at the trellis and the borders and keeps watching me. Blackbirds fly into the hedges with food. I finger the dry soil, dream of a whole world slowly becoming dust, and shudder as the day begins to close.

At dusk I am by the garden gate. I want to be carried through time, back into the hawthorn tree, back to the first ever time I nested. I want to be carried to the distant nest when the dying is done and we all are reassembled. Dad stands beside me. His hand is at the small of my back, pressing me gently forward. He smiles as he sends me out on the errand that he knows is necessary but will be in vain. I move down through the gathering dark. I hear the distant grinding of gears and engines. By the time I come to the shore I know that the convoy has travelled on, that Morlock, Corinna and the Time Machine have gone. I stand beneath the hawthorn. I see other figures at the fringes of the field, and understand that I am just one of several disappointed shades gathered on Felling Shore this night.

BARBARA'S PHOTOGRAPHS

There never had been many photographs of our sister Barbara. After she died, some well-meaning soul took away every photograph of her that existed. They have not been returned. Perhaps they have been destroyed.

I seem to remember one picture of her sitting in a wicker cradle on the dunes at Alnmouth. There is sand and marram grass around her, the sea beyond. Our mother's legs, in shiny stockings and strong shoes, enter from the edge of the photograph, and we see the fringe of the blanket she is sitting on. Barbara stretches out from the cradle and laughs towards the photographer, who is probably our father. This image, however, is confused in my mind with a similar photograph of Mary, the sister who came after Barbara, in what is probably the same wicker cradle on the green beside the sea at South Shields. And even as I write these words, I begin to wonder whether this second photograph is also misremembered, and that it is Margaret, the youngest of us all, and not Mary, who reaches out from the cradle.

It was so long ago. We were all so young. Some of us were not even born. Memory, dream, desire, imagination have mingled through the years. How is it possible to bring this sister truly back to mind?

What I see most of all is a little girl in the window of the pebble-dashed house in Thirlmere. She sits in her pram watching for me to come home from school. As I appear in the street and pass the window and enter through the gate, she sits up tall and claps her hands and laughs and laughs and there has never been such joy.

It is possible, I suppose, that her photographs will be returned, and that the clarity of such images will be enhanced, though none of us expects it now.

We each have our way of seeing her.

We will go on forever remembering her, inventing her.

JONADAB

Jonadab was our grandfather's place, a place more impossible and distant than Timbuctoo.

'Where you going?' we'd ask him.

'Jonadab,' he'd say.

'Where you been?'

'Jonadab.'

'But where's Jonadab?'

'Timbuctoo.'

I'd seen Timbuctoo on the map, in Geography. There it was in the African desert, tiny and exotic, a week's camel ride through the blazing heat from the nearest town. But Jonadab wasn't in the index of the atlas. It was nowhere. It was an invented place. It was a place to tease us, to halt our questioning, to silence us.

At school we moved lesson by lesson through the world. We coloured in the remnants of the Empire. We traced the routes of great explorers, we followed the missionaries and saints, we marked the places of conquest and conversion.

We studied the longest rivers and the highest mountains. We learned the populations of major cities, the names of the seas and the plains. We studied the way of life of the Eskimo, the Pygmy, the Arab, the Red Indian. We were shown the fringes of civilisation, the wildernesses of heat and ice and savagery beyond.

And then one term Miss Lynch arrived and our studies came home. She was a small woman who drove a small white Fiat and who had teardrops of silver dangling from her ears. We watched her in assembly and saw how she didn't say the prayers. We leaned over in our steelhinged benches and looked at her legs. She told us that we were the centre of all geography and the focus of all history. She said we were growing at the most privileged of times. We'd have been crawling through Felling Pit less than a century ago. We had a duty to understand our place in time, to keep history moving forward.

She spread maps on her desk and invited us to stand around her. We gasped to see the names of our streets in print. We stabbed our fingers on to our own houses and gardens, we traced familiar pathways through familiar streets and parks and playing fields. We located the places of great fights and football matches. We followed bus and train routes through Gateshead and over the bridges into Newcastle. She showed the shafts going down into the coalfield and the places where ships were built. We saw the great curves of the river as it made its way to the North Sea, and I caught my breath and halted, for there, in tiny letters just beyond Felling's boundary, was Jonadab Lane and then Jonadab itself: a small empty space on the banks of the Tyne.

*   *   *

When she pinned the map to the wall I sat below it and drew my route. I carefully named the familiar streets I must take: Rectory Road, Chilside Road, The Drive, Sunderland Road. I sketched the graveyard and Memorial

108

Gardens at Heworth. I marked the places where I would cross the railways and the bypass and go beyond Felling into Pelaw and then into the unknown fields below, until at the foot of my page by the crayoned blue river, I came to my map's most distant and exotic point whose name I went over time and again. Jonadab. Jonadab. Jonadab.

Miss Lynch came to me and smiled.

'You do this very well.'

'Thank you, Miss.'

Her eyelashes were dark and curved. There was pale lipstick on her lips.

'You come from a Felling family.'

'Yes, Miss.'

I showed her our house in Coldwell Park, then the other places we'd lived: Felling Square, Thirlmere, Felling Square again. I showed her our grandparents' homes in Ell Dene Crescent and Rectory Road.

'And where were the family before?'

'Don't know, Miss.'

She smiled again.

'You should ask about these things,' she said. 'You should write down everything you find. Or the memory

109

will be gone.'

She moved among us. She kept returning to me. She watched me drawing, the pencil following the shapes my finger made as it moved across the map.

'You won't understand this,' she said. 'When you travel through the place in which you were born, you travel through yourself.'

*   *   *

I set off that Saturday morning. I put bread, cheese, fruit in a haversack. I put in my map and a notebook. I told our parents that Miss Lynch said it was my duty to understand my home, and that I was going to explore for a few hours.

'Just in Felling,' I said.

They laughed and said I'd hardly be lost, then.

As I walked from the garden through the gate, Catherine called after me.

'Where you going?'

I grinned and looked back at her.

'Jonadab,' I said.

*   *   *

On Rectory Road our grandfather was watching from his window. He beckoned me over. I waved and walked on. I called that I was going to Jonadab and knew that he couldn't hear. It was early spring and crocuses were growing in the verges beneath the trees on Chilside Road. The sun was drying the pools on the pavements left by last night's showers. The distant river was gleaming between banks crammed with cranes and warehouses. The sea on the horizon was dark as ink. As I turned down on to The Drive I heard a voice calling me. I turned and waved again, to one of our aunts, one or other of the identical twins. I crossed the bypass at Heworth and paused on the high steel foot-bridge that trembled as the traffic roared beneath. I looked down across the graveyard and tried to distinguish our sister Barbara's grave and tried to recall how she had been in life. I paused again in Pelaw, in the shadow of the huge CWS buildings that lined the road there. The clash of printing machines came from inside. I nibbled some cheese and looked at the unfamiliar faces passing by. I consulted my map, walked on, turned left at Bill Quay Park into a street that suddenly steepened in descending to the Tyne. There were a few rows of terraced houses, an area of waste ground before a pub, the wide expanse of the river, shipyards filling the opposite bank, ships as tall as St Patrick's church resting there. I found the small white name plate with Jonadab Lane written in black, fixed to the wall of a low warehouse or workshop. The lane was uncared-for: broken tarmac, cobbles showing through, potholes filled with black rainwater. A slope of weeds and broken buildings hung over it. I followed it and it opened out into an empty area, a small rough field sloping to a six-foot drop to the water. Then there were factories and workplaces and houses stretching all the way to the city with its arched bridge.

Three ponies were tethered to stakes, with their heads lowered to the grass. A boy and a girl sat on a pile of stones facing the river. A small fire burned beside them, its smoke rising languidly through the clear air. A bony mongrel was tied to the stones by a rope around its neck. It growled, and the children turned to me. They leaned closer together and muttered and laughed.

'Who this?' the boy called.

They laughed again and turned to face me.

'Who this?' he repeated.

They had long sticks in their fists like spears, the tips pointed and scorched. They had sheath knives in their belts. The boy jabbed his spear at me.

'Ungowa!' he said. 'Speak!'

The girl stared. The dog growled again.

'Is this Jonadab?' I said.

'Not understand!'

They laughed.

The boy shouted, 'Shove off home!'

I stood there.

The girl took her knife from its sheath, ran her thumb over the blade. The boy lifted his pullover, pointed to a scar that slanted through the right side of his stomach to his waist. 'She do this with she knife.' He glared. 'Understand?' I nodded. 'Yes.'

'She mighty wild. You touch her and you finished. Where you come from?'

I pointed back up the hill towards Felling.

'Where your people?'

I pointed again.

They grinned at each other.

'Him all, all alone.'

The girl ran her thumb on the blade of her knife. We watched each other.

They were blond, blue-eyed, a little older than me. Tangled hair. Filthy faces. They wore jeans, broken shoes, ripped pullovers. A cooking pot and a kettle were on the blackened earth around their fire. Stuffed rucksacks and rolled-up blankets rested on the stones. Beyond them, sparks cascaded over the hull of a half-built ship. The crackle of welding rods and the voices of workmen calling to each other echoed on the water. Beneath everything was the endless low din of engines and machines, the sour scent of the river.

I stood there and felt no fear.

'Is this Jonadab?' I said again.

I took the cheese from my pocket and nibbled it.

'Him bring food,' said the boy. He beckoned me with his spear. 'Ungowa! Ungowa!'

I pulled the haversack from my shoulders and moved towards them. I showed them the bread, the cheese, the fruit. I squatted in front of them.

'You live here?' I said.

They laughed. The boy stamped on the earth.

'This sacred ground,' he said, and he stuck his spear into it.

He reached out and took some of the food. He broke some cheese and gave it to the girl. He pointed to me, to the food, invited me to join them. The girl giggled.

'Mighty good,' he said. He pointed to a rock. 'You sit, boy.'

I ate the bread and the cheese. I opened a pomegranate with my penknife and gave each of them a section.

'You're brother and sister,' I said.

She giggled again.

'Last of our people,' he said. 'Why you come here?'

I shrugged.

'Just to look.'

'This sacred ground.'

And you live here?'

'Many suns. Many moons. She and me. She mighty wild. Beware.'

He turned his face away. The girl delicately picked out the pomegranate seeds with her fingertips. She raised her eyes and stuck her tongue out at me.

'Mighty danger here,' he said. 'Bad people come. At night we see ghosts that dance on water. Sometimes the dog kids come and watch us in the dark.'

'Dog kids?'

'Children got from woman and dog together. Paws for hands and feet and hair on backs and howls like babies crying. Fire keep them away from us. And the spirits of our people come watch over us.' He lifted his spear. 'This dangerous place for you, boy.

Mebbe time go home.'

She raised her eyes. She nodded. I looked at my map.

'It is Jonadab,' I said.

I sketched the place in my notebook: the field, the stones, the broken buildings. I copied the graffiti that was carved into the stones around me: names and dates going back centuries. I thought of Miss Lynch and I built a settlement in my head: houses, a mill, a farm, stone walls enclosing a field of sheep, a little jetty joining Jonadab to the water.

'Where do you come from?' I said.

He contemplated.

'Too many questions,' he said. He swept his arm towards the horizon. 'Far far way, boy.'

'Have you been here long?'

He scowled, took a crumpled cigarette end from behind his ear, lit it in the fire and smoked. He passed it to the girl.

'Bad people come, want to take her way from me. We leave in the night. We bring horses. We ride many days to this holy place.'

He turned his face away. They laughed.

'We kill many,' he said. 'Much blood has run from our knives. We mighty wild.'

I was about to ask more, when he raised his shirt again, showed me the scar again.

'Appendicitis,' I whispered.

He stood over me with his knife in his fist.

'So what you got, boy? What blood you had? What pain you had?'

I contemplated my body, the meagre grazes on its knees, the lack of scars. My easy breath. The easy beating of my heart. I shrugged.

'Nothing.'

His face was scornful.

'Ungowa,' he said.

He turned to the girl.

'Show him,' he said.

She pulled her hair back, showed a healed gash across her temple. She lifted her pullover, showed where an area of her lower back was distorted and discoloured after burning. There were other burns, smaller, more recent, scattered on her skin.

She glared with her blue eyes.

'See,' he said.

'What happened?' I said.

He thrust his knife at me.

'Too many questions. Touch,' he said.

I laid my fingertip on the blade, felt the sharpness, how it would cut so easily.

'See,' he said.

'Yes.'

'Much danger, boy. You think you safe, but always danger coming. Why you come?'

'To look. To see.'

'Ha. Ha.'

He unfastened one of the rucksacks by the rocks. He took out a book, *The Boy's Big Book of Indians*. On its cardboard cover was a young bare-chested brave on a galloping pony. The pages inside were brittle and bleached. The faded print told of the tribes, the great plains, the freedom before the white man came. There were pictures of more braves. There were herds of buffalo, villages of teepees, ferocious chiefs, beautiful squaws with babies.

'Our people,' he said.

I looked at the girl. She stuck out her tongue. He thrust the knife at me. I nodded.

'You come look see here, boy.'

He stood up, tugged my arm, took me to the final drop to the river. We squatted at the edge. Below us was the dark slowly moving water, its slimy surface, the waste it carried. The mud above the water line was slick and shining, rainbows of oil shimmering upon it. The exposed earth higher up was cracked and crazed. He leaned over and tugged at the earth, lifted a thin splintered bone from it.

'These the bones of our people. We keep watch on them. This holy place.'

He stood up and held his hands towards the earth of Jonadab.

'The bones of our people. Somewhere here our father, somewhere here our mother.' The girl on the stones sniggered, giggled. He held the bone in his palm. 'Mebbe this a bit of mother, a bit of father. Mebbe from an older time. Mebbe from time way way back, boy.' He went to the fire, raised the bone over his head. He grunted several times, stamped his feet, muttered and wailed. His voice intensified. He howled and howled. Then was silent, sat by his sister. She stuck her tongue out.

'Now you shove off back, boy,' he said.

She nodded, formed the words with her lips: shove off back. He dropped the bone. The dog crawled to it, started to lick. The boy and the girl leaned on each other. They faced away from me. He lit another cigarette stub and they smoked together.

I sketched them. I stared towards the city, saw the huge construction cranes turning so slowly across the rooftops, saw the glint of traffic in the sunlight as it moved across the bridge, saw the world moment by moment being created on what was gone.

'I knew somebody who died,' I said.

They were lost in themselves. I imagined following them, entering their silence, moving through it step by step. Another little journey, another

Jonadab.

'I knew somebody that's in the ground,' I said.

The girl turned.

'Where that?' said the boy.

I pointed back up the hill. 'There. Up there.'

'Ha. Up there.'

I moved to them. I sat on a stone at their side.

'There's ground up there filled with people, too,' I said. The boy nodded.

'Places everywhere built on bones.'

The girl held the cigarette to me. I smoked it and my head began to reel and I smoked again.

I stood above the fire and stamped my feet and grunted. I muttered and wailed and the girl giggled. I put my hand flat to my mouth and hooted. The dog growled. The boy came to my side and stamped and hooted too. Then the girl at last. She circled the fire and held her face up to the sky. We circled the fire together and squealed and screamed.

When it was over we sat on the stones again. The girl was at my side. I wrote in my book, *I went to Jonadab today*. I closed my eyes and moved into the silence. After a long time, she whispered, 'Yes. This is Jonadab.' And then another long time, and she whispered, 'We bring the ponies for the grass.'

She leaned on me.

'We sleep out in fine weather,' she whispered. 'Our home is not far away.'

Her body rose and rested on her breath.

'Your people are good,' she said.

'Yes.'

'Write your people.'

I wrote their names: my father, my mother, my sisters, my brother.

'Write the one that's gone.'

I wrote her name, Barbara.

'Write us.'

'Who are you?'

'John and Jane.'

I wrote their names.

'Who are your people?' I asked.

'Our father died and then our mother died. We live with another, who is bad.'

The boy was silent, until he knelt

123

before us with his knife. He took our thumbs and cut into their soft flesh and squeezed out the blood. He cut his own thumb. We pressed our wounds against each other's wounds.

'Now we brothers and sisters,' he said. 'We joined in blood.'

We meditated on this.

'One day much blood will run from our knives,' said the girl. 'We will go off on the horses.'

I asked no questions. We sat there. The field by the river was quiet and still. The men in the shipyards called to each other. Sparks cascaded into the water.

'One day I thought I was going to die,' she said.

She turned. We looked together towards Jonadab Lane, and saw the dark figure waiting there below the broken buildings.

'It's nothing,' she whispered. 'Don't look. Don't ask.'

After a time she kissed my cheek.

I thought of Miss Lynch and of my duty to move forward. I thought of my sister in the ground at Heworth. I thought of the stone with her name on it, the space beneath waiting for other names. I thought of passing her, of climbing home again through familiar streets, passing familiar faces, and there came a great ache of desire to stay in Jonadab this day, and then to disappear, to ride into the unknown places with these gentle children and their beasts.

THE SUBTLE BODY

I fell in love with Theresa as I came back from kissing the cross.

It was Good Friday afternoon. St Patrick's church was packed. Babies squealed. Old women whimpered in grief. The place reeked of incense and sweat and beery breath. The priests' voices droned in prayer and wobbled in song. They went on and on about death and Hell and gloom. The day darkened and darkened and darkened. A hailstorm roared in from the North Sea.

I squirmed on my hard seat. Never again. Never again.

I was with Mick Flannery. He'd gone off to train to be a priest when he was eleven. Two months ago they'd sent him back, and he was quickly making up for lost time. It was Mick who spotted Theresa. We were shuffling to the altar. The choir was groaning through 'O Sacred Heart'.

'Corduroy suit. Black hair,' he

hissed. 'Lovely.'

She was on her way back, black mantilla draped across her head.

'An angel,' he moaned. 'Who is she?'

A mystery. I dipped my head as Father O'Mahoney held out the cross. I kissed the great black nail that pierced Christ's feet.

Going back I saw her a few rows beyond our own. Her eyes were piously downcast.

The priests said that Christ had begun his voyage through death, that like all of us he would rise again, that like all of us he would return in more glorious form.

I kept turning.

She raised her dark eyes to me, and my heart was hers.

*   *   *

Afterwards, we waited in the dusk beneath St Patrick's statue until she came. She was with a girl I knew, Mary or Maria, who lived out Heworth way. We followed them towards Felling Square then on to Watermill Lane where heavy trees grew from the verges and yellow streetlights shone down through the spring leaves.

'What can we do?' said Mick.

I started to run.

Maria held Theresa tight.

'What you after?' she asked.

'Saw you in church,' I said to Theresa. I gagged and gaped. 'Never seen anybody so beautiful.'

'She's Theresa,' said Maria. 'My cousin. She's from Winlaton.'

'Come out with me,' I said.

Mick struck a match behind me.

'She's come to be with me,' said Maria.

'All of us,' I said. You and all. Mick and all.'

They huddled together and whispered and giggled, then Theresa came in close. Her corduroy on the back of my hand, her scent, the sweetness of her breath.

'Tomorrow,' she whispered. 'Same time. Here.'

And they were gone, heels clacking through the shadows of the trees.

The back of my hand was tingling.

My spirit was soaring. 'Thanks be,' Mick said.

'Amen. Amen.'

*   *   *

Dad was still alive then. He told me I was a member of the most privileged generation the world had ever seen. There'd be nothing I couldn't do. Nothing must hold me back. We used to stand together in the garden and he talked about the war, how it had stifled his own generation. He said a time of great liberation had arrived. He understood the doubts that I was prey to: the problems of my faith, the complexity of my young body, the yearnings and confusions of my liberated mind. He said there were temptations and possibilities he had no experience of.

Mam used to cry when I questioned the faith. But he used to whisper, 'Find your own way. Go as far as you need.' He'd hold me close.

'Just don't leave us behind. You'll need us waiting here with our love.'

Then he'd ask about books, and we'd start to smile. He knew that the library had begun to overcome the church.

The library was a prefabricated place on a green beside the square. I took out armfuls of Hemingway and Lawrence and forgotten names from the Recommended New Novels section. I pored in excited confusion through *The Waste Land* and *The Cantos*. I learned Dylan Thomas and Stevie Smith by heart. I plundered the shelves of the paranormal. I devoured surveys of the occult, read tantalising accounts of spontaneous combustion, the aura, teleportation, poltergeists and human vanishings. I took home books on yoga and propped them on the bedroom floor as I attempted the Plough or the Lotus or teetered upside-down on my head. I squatted between the beds, meditated, and attempted to reach some higher plane.

I kept reading about the body's subtlety: there was the thing of bones and the thing of spirit; in between was an astral body with elements of both these forms. This body could be inhabited by adepts, who travelled in the astral plane above the material world. I wanted to do this. I wanted to learn the necessary mantras, to submit to arcane disciplines. But the references were coy and confusing, gushing descriptions, no instruction.

Then I discovered the books of T. Lobsang Rampa, my exotic counterpart, my guide. He was a Tibetan monk forced into exile by the barbaric Chinese. His map of Lhasa in *The Third Eye* was an exalted version of Felling. I imagined walking past the Potala Palace as I walked past Felling Square, loitering in Norbu Linga as I loitered in Felling Park, gazing down towards the Kyi Chu River as I gazed towards the Tyne.

Lobsang taught me that there were no secrets. Imagination was the only key. With thumping heart I read his words, so thrilling, so intimate:

As you lie alone upon your bed, keep calm. Imagine that you are gently disengaging from your body. Imagine that you are forming a body the exact counterpart of your physical body, and that it is floating above the physical, weightlessly. You will experience a slight swaying, a minute rise and fall. There is nothing to be afraid of. As you keep calm you will find that gradually your now-freed spirit will drift until you float a few feet off. Then you can look down at yourself, at your physical body. You will see that your physical and your astral bodies are connected by a shining silver cord which pulsates with life. Nothing can hurt you so long as your thoughts are pure.

Dad was with me in the living room as I read this. He smiled at the three eyes and the snowy mountains on the cover. He told me as he so often did about Burma, the wet heat and stench of the jungle, the awful fear of the Japanese.

'I saw the Himalayas once,' he said. 'Went with a mate on leave. Travelled north for days. Came one night to a station in the middle of nowhere. We sat on the platform, waiting. Lots of Indians beside us with blankets pulled over their heads. Over the line there was a fire burning and they were playing flutes and a girl was dancing. I kept thinking of your mother, of Felling, getting home again. Kept nodding off, dreaming of being here, certain I was here, then jerking awake again. The sun came up and straight away it was blazing hot and glaring and the fields were shimmering and the line was shining bright. There they were, the Himalayas, out past everything. Icy white and still and beautiful. They just drew your eyes to them and held them. Then the train came and chaos started and we were heading back again.'

He smoked and coughed and smiled again.

'Always said I'd go back there. Tibet, maybe. Nepal . . . Maybe you will, though.'

I went on reading.

If you imagine it strongly enough you can do it.

'Aye. You know there's more than this. Maybe you will.'

I couldn't do it. Too much disturbance. Not enough purity. Not enough imagination. Night after night I tried. Often I felt the minute rise and fall. I was on the point of breaking free. I imagined looking down upon Felling, lights arranged in rows along the streets, dark patches of parks and gardens, the river's gleam, all of Tyneside glittering in the night. I imagined travelling to Tibet itself, to the snowy peaks, the eagles, the palaces, the fluttering prayer flags. I imagined the shining cord stretching back to the bony body on the bed. But each night I lay surrounded only by the known and the familiar: the small house, the darkness, Dad's snoring, one of my sisters murmuring in her sleep.

And on Good Friday Theresa disturbed my imaginings: her dark hair and eyes, her sweetness and her breath, and my anticipation of tomorrow.

*   *   *

Mick and I stood beneath the trees. We breathed smoke through the mist towards the lights.

'Tell me about the Fathers,' I said.

'Why's it always that you want to know?'

'Were there things you can't talk about?'

'Things?'

'Secrets. Things they taught you. Things they showed you.'

'We did Latin all the time. They told us about Africa and malaria. They went on and on about Hell. They showed us how to lie in bed in an attitude of prayer. We had to contemplate our end and rise above the flesh.'

'And did you?'

'All we talked about was girls. All we imagined was girls.' He had the wildness in his eyes that had come back from the Fathers with him.

'They asked about our dreams. They searched our lockers, read our letters. They were evil, man.'

The girls didn't come. We scanned the houses, looked for the Sacred

Heart medallions in the doorlights that showed where Catholics were. We cursed and blasphemed. Then there was a door ajar, a crack of light inside the frame, music playing. We stepped through the gate.

Mick gripped my am.

'You have the pretty one,' he said. 'I saw the way she looked at you. I'll have the other. Right?'

I peered through the doorlight, past the medallion's silhouette. From inside carne the singing of Smokey Robinson and the Miracles.

'Must be them,' he said. He rapped on the door. Hurrying feet and laughter, then Maria, peering out.

'What you doing?' she asked.

'You said you'd come.'

'How d'you know we wouldn't?'

'We waited.'

'And we're not worth waiting for?'

'Let's come in.'

Theresa Came, stood in the hall.

'They want to come in,' laughed Maria.

She sniggered, then let us through. I saw Christ exposing his heart for us. I smelt Theresa, felt her hand brush against mine.

'Nobody in?' said Mick.

Maria laughed.

'They're at the vigil.'

We drank sherry that tasted like altar wine. The girls sat on a sofa and Mick and I on deep chairs. Smokey finished and the Temptations slapped down on to the turntable. There was a statue of the Virgin Mary on the mantelpiece. Plaster angels flew across the walls. We tapped our cigarettes relentlessly on the rims of ashtrays. Theresa talked about Winlaton, in the hills beyond Felling. So rough, lads fighting in the streets all the time. She'd dreamed for weeks of coming here.

'But I can't stay long,' she said, and she gazed into my eyes.

Mick left me and sat on the sofa with his arm around Maria. Theresa smiled and turned the light off and came to me and we kissed.

'I hoped you'd come,' she whispered.

We kissed again.

'Don't be scared,' she said.

I imagined floating through the

room, seeing the two of us tangled below me on the armchair.

'Keep calm,' whispered Theresa.

I ran my hands across her.

'Not too far,' she whispered.

We lay sighing.

'I'm glad you were in the church,' she whispered. 'You believe in it?'

'It?'

'God. Sin. Angels. Hell and Heaven. Soul and body. All that. The Cross. That He came back from death and ascended into Heaven.'

'No.'

'Me neither.'

'You like my body?' she whispered.

I sighed and my heart raced.

'Yes. I believe in astral bodies, as well,' I said.

'Astral bodies?'

'They're like souls. You float out of yourself and travel in the astral plane. It's true. All it takes is imagination.

She sniggered.

'Imagine it,' I said. 'Close your eyes. Imagine that we're rising together from the chair, that we can look down at ourselves. Imagine it. It can happen. It can really happen.'

'I'm floating,' she murmured.

For a moment it seemed true. We felt Lobsang's swaying, we began to rise from the chair. We held each other tight and kissed. Then Maria called.

'Hey. You two.' She giggled. 'Come back to the real world. Time to go.'

We went into the night, all four of us. Theresa pressed against me as we walked.

I told her about Lobsang, Tibet, the Himalayas, the astral plane.

Our breath glowed and thickened beneath the lights. Our lips were tender. We hid in the shadows as families moved past us from the vigil. Soon Maria said they'd have to go. Theresa drew me into a heavy overhanging hedge and we kissed again.

*   *   *

I walked with Mick through the mist to Felling Square. I could still smell her, feel her skin, hear her breath in my ear. Mick trembled and skipped in excitement.

'Wow,' he kept saying. 'Wow. How far'd you go?' he said.

I smiled.

'Far enough.'

'Aye. Far enough.'

We smoked a cigarette beside the fountain then went our separate ways into the gloom.

'You weren't at the vigil,' said Mam as I entered the house.

I turned my eyes down.

'Your faith's your most precious thing,' she said.

'I know that.'

I felt sure they must catch the smell of Theresa that surrounded me. I stared at our statues and angels. A rosary lay in a little heap on the mantelpiece.

'I was talking about your Tibetan bloke in the club,' said Dad. It seems he's a Kerry man that's not set foot outside Ireland.'

'I've seen that. Nobody's certain, though.'

He smiled.

'He's the real thing to you.'

'Yes.'

That night as I slept I travelled over Felling. Theresa raised her arms to welcome me. Our bodies mingled like breath in mist, like angels are supposed to, like astral bodies must.

* * *

Easter Sunday morning: the empty tomb, the risen body, the defeat of death, the resurrection of us all. We wore spring clothes and sunlight poured through the windows. Mick was at my side. Close by was Theresa, her eyes so warm each time I turned to her.

The priest held out the body and blood. We lowered our eyes and Mick muttered about Maria. At the altar rail I knelt by Theresa.

'We'll go off on our own,' she whispered. 'We'll leave the others.'

She opened her mouth, she waited for the bread. 'Yes,' I hissed.

We tilted our heads back, closed our eyes, waited to have Christ's body pressed to our tongues.

I knelt afterwards with my head

bowed in thanksgiving. I told Mick he should take Maria somewhere on his own. He grinned.

'Aye,' he whispered. 'Then get together later, eh? See where we got to.'

She waited for me in the courtyard. We sidled through the released congregation. We were almost clear when someone tapped me on the shoulder. I turned and there was Dad, smiling at us.

'Who's your friend?' he asked.

'Theresa,' I said. 'Maria's cousin. She's from Winlaton.'

He shook her hand. I stood speechless. He gently laughed, gripped my shoulder, at once holding me and pushing me away.

'Go on, then,' he said. 'On your way, son.'

We held hands on the High Street and moved across the square. Such changes: high thin drifting clouds, immaculate light. We walked up Felling Bank, densely-packed houses on either side. Children squealed in hidden gardens. I led her to Windy Ridge, sloping terraced street with allotments in front and huge playing fields beyond. Scents of wood smoke from gardeners' fires, sun on bare earth, early flowers. Men bending, touching buds, talking with each other over flower beds and vegetable plots. Sun glinting on the greenhouses. Theresa said it was so beautiful here, like somewhere foreign. There were families walking through the fields, boys engrossed in football games. I pointed down to the roof of my home, to Maria's place, to St Patrick's steeple. We traced the gleaming river through the banks of the city to the dark sea. The horizon was dead still, dead clear. I asked if she read and she said she loved modern poetry, French novels, she wanted to know about the Russians. She said that one day she'd write novels of her own, and not about Winlaton. I told her about Stevie Smith and Lawrence. I said she must read *The Third Eye*, she must learn of Lobsang, his family, his education, how his occult powers were awakened. We talked of the wideness of the world, the narrowness of our homes. We passed the remnants of the abandoned colliery, the broken concrete gun emplacement left from the war. We took a path that led from the fields into the Heather Hills. Wild daffodils. Bracken and fern unfurling. Long strings and clusters of spawn in the ponds. The yellow buds of gorse, the white of hawthorn.

We lay on a grassy slope and looked down over everything. We lay face upward side by side and watched the clouds drifting. Invisible larks were singing high above.

'We can imagine anything,' I said.

We kissed each other.

'We can go anywhere,' she said.

We kissed and kissed. We held each other, subtle body and subtle body. We rocked and swayed and lifted and fell, and we began to leave ourselves, entangled there together in the sunlight on the grass.

BEHIND THE BILLBOARDS

Stoker's been after us for days. None of us knows why. Somebody must have been spinning stories about us, telling lies. There's four of us: Mickey, Tash, Coot, and me. We're sure we've done nothing wrong and said nothing wrong.

'But that's it,' says Tash. 'With him you don't need to. He believes what he wants to believe. That's why he's so wild.'

*   *   *

This morning we're kicking about on Felling Banks when Mickey sees him in the distance, coming up from the Old Fold with his dog.

'Don't look like you're running,' he tells us. 'Just get the ball and move.'

We look back from where the new flats are on Wellington Street. There's Stoker coming in a dead straight line across the field. There's the dog on a tight chain at his side.

145

'Maybe he doesn't know it's us,' says Coot.

We just look at him. We move on. We can't help running once we think we're out of Stoker's sight. At the square, we climb in behind the billboards and wait for him to pass.

Coot's already crying. He's kneeling in the dirt and the litter that's been shoved through the lattice underneath the boards. There's tears splashing down from his eyes.

'He slashed Malcolm Rowel's tongue,' he says. 'He made him stick it out and he slit it, right at the tip. He said, "Tell-tale tit. Don't tell your tales about me. Next time I'll cut it off"'

He holds his hand across his mouth and he sobs and gasps. 'And what if he comes in here?' he says.

We say nothing. We just look at each other then at this place, this narrow gap between the high billboards and the high wall of Dobey's warehouse. Stupid. The only way out's the way we've come in.

'What if he does?' says Coot.

Tash gets his penknife and thumbs

the blade out. 'Shut up,' he says. 'Or I'll do the job myself.'

But we know Coot's right, and we're just about to jump out again when we see Stoker heading out from the flats. We crouch there. We hardly breathe. Coot starts blabbering to Our Lady till Tash points the knife at his throat.

'Shut up, Coot. The dog'll hear you. It'll smell your fear.'

I feel how I'm trembling, how my heart's racing. My palms are slippery with sweat. I watch the knife point digging into Coot's white skin as Stoker and the dog pass by the gap. Coot's prayer starts running through my head.

Hail Mary, full of . . .

Coot's a bastard. We didn't know what the word meant till we found out the truth about Coot. His mother was young and stupid and she used to go with anybody. There's a man with them sometimes but he's not Coot's father and Coot's mother's not his wife. The story is he goes to sea and they'll marry when he's back at shore for good, but it's like the story they used to tell when we were young that his first dad died.

We're told to pray for them but even we can see how they might be past all help.

Coot's an altar boy like the rest of us. He got his name when he was an acolyte on Passion Sunday and the candle set his hair on fire and he ran screaming off the altar. The priest chased him into the vestry and clipped him and asked what he was doing defiling the feast in such a way. Tash who's a couple of years older than us laughed and said it was an early visit from the flames of Hell. There were great bald patches on Coot's skull and that's how afterwards he was known as Coot. He used to whinge and tell us not to call him that, but pretty soon he gave up. He knows that this is how things probably will always be.

He's OK really. He gets fags from his mother and shares them out. He doesn't mind when we hang about in his street just to get a look at her. There's something about him that means you can talk to him. He was the only one that put his arm around me and whispered he was sorry when my little sister died.

*   *   *

Mickey passes a packet of Player's round. We make sure we blow the smoke upwards so it drifts away invisible over the top of the boards. We sit leaning against Dobey's wall. We lean sideways so we can see out through the lattice into the square. We know we'll be impossible to see. Stoker's on a bench right in the middle. He lets the dog gobble at his fingers and even from this distance, thirty yards or so, we can see its saliva dripping and dribbling.

We get calmer and bolder. Mickey sticks his fingers up and whispers, 'Clear off; Stoker.' Tash pees against the back of the boards and says he's peeing all over the dog. We test each other to see if we can remember what's on the front of the boards. Tash says one of them's for Peter Stuyvesant. Mickey says there's a woman in a tight dress but he's never bothered to read what she's selling.

149

'It's Omo,' says Coot. 'Washes whiter, drives out stains.' Even he has to laugh when Tash tells him to get out and check them all.

Then we settle down, because there's an old bloke sitting on a bench close by. He's eating a pie from Myers, and he's got a dog as well, a Jack Russell that tilts its head and peers at the boards like it's heard us.

We sit there quiet. We watch the traffic and the walkers, the dozens of familiar faces passing through the square. Sometimes we murmur a name, or pass quick judgement: he's a mean old git, there's talk she'll die soon, lovely legs.

Stoker doesn't move.

In here there's never any proper light and nothing grows. The ground's dry and dusty. There's ancient cigarette packets, cigarette butts, brick dust and dry mortar that's fallen from the wall, little jagged stones. Soon Coot's whispering his prayers again. When he catches us listening he says Our Lady of Fatima's the one to pray to. She appeared only to children, he says.

Tash laughs. She's the one there's that statue of at St Andrew's, he says. You can see the shape of her body underneath her dress. Coot chews his nails and says nothing. Mickey passes the fags around again and they're dry. It's like smoking the dust.

Tash watches Coot.

'He still believes it all,' he says. 'Can't see through any of it.'

'Why's he bloody after us?' says Mickey.

Tash runs his penknife blade back and forward across his jeans.

'There's four of us and one of him,' he says, but we know he knows that's useless.

'God,' he whispers. He stabs the blade into the earth. He laughs. 'Stick your tongue out, Coot,' he whispers.

We see Father O'Mahoney hurrying through the square. He's got his black-fringed stole on.

'Somebody's kicking it,' says Mickey.

Coot crosses himself and shakes his head.

We watch the old bloke feeding the last of his pie to his dog.

'I'm starving,' I say. 'Run out and buy us a pie, Coot.'

Then I see the tears in his eyes, and I touch his arm.

'Clear off, Stoker,' I whisper.

'What have we done to him?' I ask.

We talk about making a run for it, jumping out and scattering, but we know it's useless, none of us would want to be the one that's caught.

'Maybe we're wrong,' says Coot. 'Maybe he isn't after us at all.'

'Get out, then,' says Tash, and he laughs and smiles. 'Go on, jump down.'

He watches Coot, strops the knife.

'Why does it make you so happy to see him so sad?' I say. Tash shrugs and spits.

'Because he's a bastard and I'm OK.'

He smiles again.

'Isn't that right, Coot?' he says.

Coot closes his eyes, moves his lips in silent prayer.

Tell us about your dad,' says Tash. Was he a damned bastard as well?'

Mickey calms it down. He hushes us, points out at the Jack Russell that's facing us, eyes and ears all alert.

Beyond it, Stoker doesn't move. His dog lounges on the bench beside him. The sun's shining down on everything out there.

'Tell us,' says Tash, more quietly. 'Tell us a story, Coot. Tell us where you came from and where you think you're headed. Tell us the truth, not the lies you used to spread.'

'Tash,' I whisper.

'What?' he says.

I stare at the boards. I try to remember what's on them. I try to imagine what Stoker thinks we've said. I think of the story of Malcolm Rowell's tongue and I know it's true. I've seen the healed slit when he puts his tongue out for the priest to place Communion on it. I wonder what we've done and what we'll do and I find my lips moving almost automatically, seeking intercession from Our Lady.

'Maybe Coot's right,' I murmur. 'Maybe he isn't after us at all.'

The others say nothing. We're silent for what seems an age, till Coot begins to cry again.

'I wasn't lying,' he says. 'I used to

believe everything I was told and everything I said. I believed it so much I could even remember him. I saw what he looked like. I heard his voice. I remembered being small and being with him. I remembered how happy I was when he was there. And then I found out I was wrong. There was no way I could remember. But I wasn't telling lies.'

We wait, and we listen to the traffic and the footsteps outside.

'It wasn't the truth,' says Tash at last.

He strops the knife and spits.

'She wanted to keep things secret,' says Coot. 'She didn't want me to suffer because of her past.'

'Secrets!' says Tash.

'Yes!' says Coot. 'Secrets. Even Our Lady of Fatima had secrets, things that had to be kept hidden, things for nobody but the children to know.'

Mickey hushes them again. The Jack Russell's on its feet, tugging at its lead. We see Stoker, so calm, not moving. 'And what about now?' whispers Tash. 'What's the secrets now? What's she get up to when he's home with her?

What do you get up to, Coot?'

'Jesus, Tash!' I whisper.

He points the knife at Coot's throat.

'One day he'll stop his travelling,' says Coot. 'Then he'll marry her and he'll be my father. I know he will.'

'You see it, do you?' says Task 'Just like you saw the first happy little family. Just like when you were telling all those lies.'

The Jack Russell yaps, tugs at its lead. The old bloke stares towards us.

'You been spreading stories about Stoker, Coot?' says Tash.

Coot gasps, yelps.

'Stick your tongue out, Coot,' says Tash.

Coot stares at me, then pushes past me. He jumps down through the gap.

We lie in the dry dust and look out through the lattice as Coot hurries across the square. We see Stoker rising calmly from the bench. He tugs the dog to its feet. They follow Coot down in the direction of the Old Fold.

We wait for a few moments in silence, then we jump down. We don't look at each other as we go our

155

separate ways. I hurry uphill towards home. When I'm clear of the square I slow down. My heart beats more gently, I breathe more easily. Already I'm starting to feel happiness through the shame.

CHICKENS

He watched me walk clumsily through the rows of lettuce towards him. He sat against the greenhouse wall as always. He wore his serge suit and his cloth cap as always. He smoked his pipe. He'd have been there for an age. He'd have been listening to the blackbirds and the skylarks, dreaming, watching, waiting. Now he leaned forward, raised his hand, knocked out the pipe against the building's wooden frame, and allowed himself to smile.

'Grand start to your holiday, then?'

I sat beside him on the bricks that had lain unmoved for years against the glittering building. I leaned at ease against the warm glass, sniffed the familiar scents of tobacco and earth.

'Brilliant,' I murmured.

'Aye,' he said. 'And the big un's coming?'

I shrugged. Colin was still in bed.

'The tomatoes ready?' I asked, and he smiled again.

'No. But there's some late chickens hatched out. Come and see.'

The first door opened into a dark and musty interior. The cracked floor was littered with tools and plant-pots, great sacks of compost and peat. Rusted implements hung untouched from year to year on the walls. Empty rat traps lay in the corners. I picked my way past the obstacles and opened the door of the greenhouse itself, entered the sudden brightness and heat, breathed the sweet powdery scent of tomatoes. I went to a large cardboard box and put my hand inside. I laughed at the tiny voices and the tiny feet that scratched my skin. I lifted one of the chicks and held it bright yellow to my face.

'Can this one be mine?' I asked.

He laughed.

'Aye, that can be yours,' he said.

I stared. It would grow so quickly. It would be just another unshapely squawking thing that strutted in the henhouse. He touched my cheek and we were silent until he asked, 'Your mam's all right, then?'

'She's fine. She wants a lettuce, if there's any.'

'Plenty. And flowers for her as well. Come on.'

I replaced the bird, pausing to see if I could distinguish that single yellow bird among so many.

Outside, I felt his eyes upon me as I crouched in the lettuce bed.

'Try to bring the big un round,' he said.

'Aye,' I said.

I felt his touch on my shoulder, heard his murmuring. 'Good lad. Aye, good lad.'

We waded into the chrysanthemums and cut a huge bunch of flowers. We wrapped them in newspaper, and he set me off, bearing these gifts to his only daughter.

*   *   *

It was a short walk between the garden and the house. Narrow Windy Ridge then Rectory Road with the broad verges and the overhanging trees, then the lane into our ring of houses. The

159

street was covered with dust. Sunlight lay flat against the dark red walls, it glittered on the windows. The shadows cast were angular and black.

'Where you goin'?'

I looked around. Ken and Terry Hutchinson stood at their front door. I turned and walked on.

'Where you been?'

I said nothing, wanted nothing to do with them. It was Ken who was calling, the oldest. Ken strode around the estate like a man and all the younger children knew, without understanding, the squalid rumours about him. I walked on until I heard them on the pavement behind.

'Hey, Ken,' said Terry. 'Look. Flowers!'

'Aye. Flowers!' said Ken.

Colin had told me never to run. I turned and Terry grabbed the parcel and spilt the flowers and the lettuce across the ground. I reached for him but Ken came to his side and with his black pointed boots he began to grind the flower heads to pulp. He kicked the lettuce and it burst and scattered on to the roadway.

He pointed into my eyes.

'Next time we speak, don't bloody well ignore us. Right?'

*   *   *

'There's plenty left in the garden,' my mother said. 'Don't let that lot worry you.'

When I went upstairs, Colin was still in bed. He told me to pass his jeans from the door. I threw them to him and sat on the window-ledge. I flicked through a football magazine while he lay cursing and struggling to pull the narrow legs of the jeans across his heels.

'Coming to the garden today?' I asked.

He shrugged. He might. He went to the wardrobe and put on his yellow shirt and watched himself in the mirror. I started to tell him what had happened in the street. He turned. Nobody picked on his brother. Where had I seen them? I answered vaguely. It wasn't revenge I wanted. If Colin

161

came back with me now, we might meet them on the way, I said. But he turned to the mirror again, and said he might come later.

'You go back,' he said. 'We'll fix the Hutchies later.'

*   *   *

My grandfather took his pipe out of his mouth and spat at the earth. The Hutchies. Always a bad lot, and there were lettuce aplenty. He smiled and touched my cheek. Nothing to worry about.

'He didn't come, then,' he said.

The morning passed quietly. I fed the hens. I wiped feathers and mud from their shells, placed them in cardboard trays in the greenhouse. Together, we watered and weeded a patch of leeks. The day grew warmer and he sent me to the shop for lemonade. We shared the bottle, wiping its rim before lifting it to our lips. I turned away smiling when I saw how the liquid drew sweat from the old man's skin. It stood in droplets above

162

his tightly-fastened collar, ran in thin trickles from below his tightly-fitting cap.

When the distant factory sirens started to howl, I exclaimed at how quickly this morning had passed.

'Aye,' he said. 'Not long till you're at that new school of yours.'

'No,' I said, and I heard the sudden trembling in my voice. We parted at the gate.

'See you this afternoon, then?' he said.

I nodded.

'Aye.'

He turned towards the club across the fields, where as always he'd spend an hour or two with old friends. I set off for home with fresh flowers and a lettuce under my arm.

*   *   *

A scorching afternoon had settled on the estate. Children played in the gardens, on the verges, in the meagre shadows of young trees. Front doors were wide open. Old people in battered sun hats sat in the shade at the sides of their homes. There were prams in many gardens, shades drawn up, chrome trimmings sparkling. There was the scent of many lunches, the hiss of bubbling fat, the chink of pots and cutlery. I hurried on, until my own name was added to the sounds that mingled in the air.

I looked around, shaded my eyes with my arm. It came again, and I saw Colin, sitting with the Hutchies outside their house. He got up and came towards me. He put his arms around my shoulders and he tugged me quickly, clumsily. The yellow shirt sleeve was brittle and crisp against my flesh.

'I saw them about it,' he said. 'It meant nothing. They'll not do it again.'

I tried to pull away.

'You coming home?' I said.

He held on to me. Then Ken came, and he also put his hand on my shoulder.

'It was nowt,' he said. 'We're sorry. We were just messing about.'

I couldn't speak. When I turned my

head, I saw the men walking into the estate, coming home for lunch. In the distance, the road surface was a glistening black pond. The voices of the others were lowered in rapid discussion, then Colin said,

'Stay with us a bit. Come on. Come with us.'

He held me closer. Terry ran to join us.

'We going, then?' he said.

'Aye,' said Ken. 'He's away.'

*　　　*　　　*

We left the estate, crossed Rectory Road, entered narrow Windy Ridge. Ken took something from his pocket, a rectangular box wrapped in brown paper. He held it teasingly, between his forefinger and thumb. I tried to grin, but the edges of my mouth twitched and I could meet none of the others' eyes. I wanted to scorn these others who could think something so special in this. But I said nothing, and I stumbled through the rubble with them, clutching the flowers and the

165

lettuce, keeping close to Colin.

'We're going to the garden,' he said, and he looked away quickly.

At the allotments, Terry ran and threw the gate open. Ken tried to push me through, but I stood my ground.

'Chicken?' he said.

'It's OK,' said Colin, taking my arm gently. 'Nobody will know.'

We walked in. Terry was already inside. He'd found the box of chicks and was poking them and laughing at them. I told him to leave it. I raised my fists, ready for anything, but Ken stepped in.

'Yeah,' he said. 'Stop messing about.'

I laid the box of chicks back on the shelf in the sunlight. I closed the door between the sunlight and the dark. Ken went to the only window and pulled aside the square of cloth that covered it. I stood watching as the others crouched in the pool of light. Ken passed some cigarettes round and I took one and watched the smoke I breathed coiling and spiralling with the dust. Then Ken lay his packet face up on the floor. A photograph of a woman was on its lid. She was dressed in thin yellow nylon, its edges drawn back to show unnaturally pink buttocks and legs. Her head was turned and she looked out with a fixed grin towards us.

'Hell,' said Colin. 'I thought it was fags.'

Ken snorted. He beckoned me down.

'Here. Get an eyeful.'

I crouched with them as Ken opened the box and lifted out the pack of cards. He started dealing them out, slowly, teasingly. He sighed and squeaked as each new woman was exposed. He touched breasts and lips and buttocks delicately with his fingers. I couldn't take my eyes away. I waited for one woman who did not arrange her limbs or her clothing to keep the secrets of her body out of sight.

Terry giggled. Ken leered and groaned. Colin was silent. I felt the sweat on my skin and heard the drumming of my heart. I looked at the women, then I looked around this darkened room, at the ancient tools, the sacks of compost, the empty rat traps. I watched the dust falling

167

endlessly through the wedge of light. I heard the high-pitched cheeping of the chicks next door. I listened for my grandfather's footsteps on the cinder path outside. I stubbed my cigarette into the dust and stared at Colin.

'Colin,' I said.

He nodded.

'That's enough,' he said.

'What's up?' said Ken.

Colin grabbed Ken's collar.

'Enough, I said. Time to go.'

I watched them, in bitter silence as they faced each other. I saw my brother's angry eyes, his clenched fist at the other's throat, his yellow shirt almost luminous in the dark. I heard his whispered threats and curses. Terry scuttled out of reach. Then Colin stood up and Ken squirmed on the floor to collect the cards.

As he left, Ken let his heel dig into my side.

'Chicken,' he whispered. 'Little chicken.'

We cleared up the cigarette ends, burned them on a small fire. We flapped the door of the greenhouse to clear the air. As we walked home, Colin put his arm around my shoulder. We paused on the waste ground.

'Didn't know what was going on,' he said.

'It's all right,' I said.

But I couldn't move. I watched the men leaving the estate, heading back to work. The houses shimmered in the heat. A crow nearby thrust its beak at something bloody in a sack. I didn't want to go home.

*   *   *

The house was stifling and steam-filled. Our mother was preoccupied. She told us to hunt out dirty clothes, told us to keep out from under her feet.

We sat down to plates of limp salad and ate in silence. Then she called me from the kitchen.

'Did you get the lettuce?'

It was in the greenhouse. It lay with the flowers beside the box of chicks.

'We'll need it for tea,' she said, and she came to the doorway.

I held the cutlery tight, pressed my

fists on the table's edge. 'It's at the garden,' I tried to say.

'Eh?'

My tongue was thick and clumsy, too big for my mouth. 'It's at the garden.'

She said my name. She leaned forward and touched my amt.

'It's all right. You can get it later.'

She watched me, said my name again.

'What is it?' she said.

THE FUSILIER

It was Margaret who told us that Mary had gone.

It was a Saturday morning, one of those we all remember, blackbirds singing in the hedges, sunlight pouring down into our small back garden. I was at the back step, eating toast. Catherine had taken some breakfast to Mam, who was still upstairs. God knows where Colin was.

Margaret was on the swing, pushing herself sluggishly back and forward. I saw the tears on her face, how she'd used her hair to try to dry them.

'What's up?' I said. I looked around the garden. 'Where's Mary?'

She sobbed helplessly, then caught her breath.

'Mary's gone,' she said. 'She's run away to join the Fusiliers.'

* * *

The Felling Fusiliers. They were a

street band from the bottom end of town, one of the hundreds of bands that existed in those days, gathering each Saturday at festivals and fêtes, pouring out of double-decker buses in tunics and glittering helmets to march through our towns behind their banners. They were led by girls with long pale legs throwing maces, and they filled the air with the rattle of drums and the squeal of kazoos. Mary'd been begging all summer to join them. She'd wrapped a broom handle in silver foil and practised for hours, spinning it and catching it. She had her own kazoo and gave us endless renditions of 'Z Cars' and 'Colonel Bogey' and 'She Loves You'. Back and forward she would march across the lawn, lifting her knees so high, holding her arms so stiff and her head so still and determined. She persuaded Margaret to join her sometimes, but the youngest sister was still awkward in her movements, she tripped and stumbled and couldn't keep up, she kept dodging away from the flying broom handle, she complained that the kazoo's vibrations stung her lips, and so often she ended rocking on the swing in tears.

*   *   *

'The Fusiliers?' I said. 'But when?'

But Margaret's voice had gone. She just stared helplessly from streaming eyes.

Catherine came to my side. We listened, and we heard Mam's slow footsteps creaking on the stairs.

'Her legs are awful this morning,' she said. 'We can't let her know about this.'

'Tell her we're going for a walk,' I said. 'Tell her we'll be back in half an hour.'

I stepped down into the garden. I called Margaret from the swing and took her hand. Catherine went in and came out again. We heard Mam calling after us to enjoy ourselves, that it was a great day for walking, that she'd be out with us herself if only she could.

We went through the gate. Catherine dabbed Margaret's eyes with a handkerchief and took her hand. We turned down the hill towards Felling Square.

* * *

I knew as we went down the wide road towards the square, with the town spread out below us and the river shining far below, that each of us was thinking of the sister who had truly gone: Barbara, the sister after Catherine, who'd been too good to stay with us for long, and who'd been so quickly taken back by God. That had been before Mary and Margaret had even arrived, but even they shared the joy of her short life and the pain of her absence. And I knew too that we thought of Dad, who'd died as well with such suffering once all of us were gathered, and whose disappearance haunted all our days. We walked down hand-in-hand and gripped each other tight. We said nothing. We knew that another loss might cause a pain that was unbearable.

* * *

As we came to Felling Square we saw Colin. There he was in his combat jacket, inside Dragone's, smoking cigarettes and drinking coffee and tapping his fingers on the table with his long-haired friends. The noise of the Rolling Stones poured through the window. We stood and watched, and for a moment in my fascination I forgot my runaway sister.

Margaret tugged my hand.

'Should we get him?'

'I don't know.'

'He'd know what to do.'

He didn't see us. We didn't go in. Too young, too timid, too shy.

'I know what to do,' I said. 'Come on.'

And we pressed on across the square, past the fountain and the flower beds, headed further down through the steep High Street, where many times men and women called out to us, their bright greetings filled with affection and tinged with familiar sympathy. We paused once more, outside St Patrick's, where we crossed ourselves and said a silent prayer that God would lead Mary safely back to us.

At the bottom of the hill, we took the footbridge across the railway line, we walked through the terraces towards the Fusiliers' field, we began to hear them, and then at last we saw them, marching across the green. The banner, the long-legged girl throwing the mace, the ranks of children in perfect formation with kazoos at their lips or drums at their waists, lifting their knees so high, holding their heads so still and so proud. At the edges of the field parents leaned on the fences and applauded, dogs yelped, boys kicked footballs across pitches marked with shirts and pullovers. Toddlers stumbled like Margaret had, trying to imitate the band. On the road outside, two red double-decker buses waited.

Stupidly, as if she'd already be dressed in purple with a white helmet, I stared into the Fusiliers, seeking her. I tugged the girls forward, urging them to peel their eyes, and felt my own eyes turning time and time again to the girl with the mace. It was Catherine who saw Mary, of course. She was sitting all alone beneath a hawthorn tree with her broom handle on the grass beside her and the kazoo gripped in her fist. She looked up as we went to her, and though her lips were trembling, her eyes were filled with rage.

'They didn't want me,' she said. 'They said I couldn't come.'

She thumped the grass and stared with longing towards the Fusiliers, who played a final chorus of 'She Loves You', then tugged off their helmets and began to climb into the buses cheered on by the parents.

'They're off to Hebburn Fair,' she said. She thumped the ground again as the engines started. 'They're going to win a silver cup. They said Mam would have to come with me if I want to join.' Each of us looked down and thought of Mam, who hadn't been out for weeks because of her legs.

'And she can't do that!' said Mary, lifting her broom handle and getting up to join us. 'She can't do that.'

The buses drove away, the parents left the field.

'Maybe I could come with you,' I said reluctantly. 'Or Colin. Or . . .'

But she just looked at me, and we knew it was hopeless, that none of us had any understanding of her fascination, that it was only Mam who'd ever give up time for such a thing. I shrugged, and Margaret took Mary's hand, and Catherine comforted them both.

Now there were only the footballers, the dogs and us, and the high sun pouring down.

'Let's go,' I said, and back we went through the terraces and over the railway line and on to the High Street. At St Patrick's we prayed again, this time in thanksgiving, though we could see that Mary still wished she was in the double-decker bus, and that she scowled when we said she'd have to tell the priest in confession what she'd done today.

In Felling Square we paused and drank at the fountain and splashed our faces and kept on smiling at the folk who greeted us.

'You'll just have to keep on

practising in the garden,' I said. 'Till she's strong enough to come with you. You understand?'

Mary shrugged, spun the broom handle between her fingers, flicked it from one hand to the other.

'They wouldn't even let me show how good I am,' she said. As we headed on, Colin came out from Dragone's towards us.

'Where you lot been?' he said.

We said nothing. He stared at us.

'What's been going on?'

Margaret's tears started again.

'Mary ran away to join the Fusiliers,' she said. 'We've been to get her back.'

Colin pushed his hair back from his eyes, took his cigarettes from his combat jacket. His friends were watching from Dragone's door. He lit a cigarette. We watched the smoke seething from his teeth.

'Bad girl,' he said at last. He wagged his finger at Mary. 'You're a bad bad girl.'

Mary hung her head. The others looked at me.

'Yes,' I said. You've been a bad girl,

Mary. You must never do it again.'

I bit my lips. This was what it was like to be fatherly, then.

'Bad girl,' I said again.

Colin nodded in approval.

'Don't do it again,' I said. 'You understand?'

Margaret nudged her.

'Yes,' she muttered. 'I understand.'

Colin held his cigarette towards me.

'Want a couple off?'

'Aye.'

I stepped forward, sucked the harsh smoke, coughed, sucked again and quickly blew it out. The girls stood hand-in-hand, watching and waiting.

'It looked bad,' I said. 'But I sorted it out.'

'Good lad.'

I looked at the smoke curling from the cigarette between my fingers, at the old boys gathered at Dragons door, heard the distant Rolling Stones.

'Nice fag,' I said, drawing again, letting the smoke out through my teeth, then passing it to him. 'I'd better take them back now.'

'Go on, then.'

I hesitated.

'Maybe I'll come down later,' I said.

He pushed his hair again and looked at me. 'Aye,' he said. 'Maybe you will.'

*   *   *

We headed back up the hill.

'You could start your own band,' I said. 'You and Margaret and Catherine.'

I stared at Margaret and Catherine, saw the looks on their faces. I raised my finger. 'Yes. You understand?'

Inside the garden, I said, 'Go on, then, Mary. Show them how it's done.'

She hung her head and for a moment just stood there beside the swing and looked despairingly at the grass, but in the end she spun the broom handle once or twice and she blew through the kazoo.

'That's great,' I said. 'But let's have more life in it. Think of those Fusiliers.'

I put them in order, Mary with the broom handle, Margaret with the kazoo, Catherine clapping her hands like a drum, and though at first their marching and music were stumbling and distressed by the morning's events, and though I knew that Margaret would soon be sitting on the swing, and that Catherine would lose patience, for a time the knees were raised and the heads were held high and the music really did sound for a short time like 'She Loves You'.

I stood beside them in the sunlight and felt the joy of being there and of having brought our sister back unharmed. I tasted the enticing bitterness of the cigarette on my tongue. My thoughts kept turning to the long pale legs of the girl with the mace. Then I saw that Mam was at the window, looking out and smiling.

'Look!' I called to her. 'Aren't they great!'

I saw the joy in her, saw her mouth say, Yes.

'Go on, girls,' I said. 'You're doing great! Look, Mam. Aren't they wonderful . . .!'

*　　　*　　　*

It was all so long ago. Now Mam's dead, and Dad died all those years ago, and Barbara was taken before two of us were even born. We who are left still come from all parts of the country to gather together near our old home. Often we tell our children about the day Mary ran away to join the Fusiliers. Sometimes we persuade her to perform for us, and then she hitches up her skirt and holds her arms so stiff and her head so still, and she marches back and forward through the room, tooting the old tunes, and we laugh and laugh, and the children giggle, and point in fascination at the tears in our eyes.

MY MOTHER'S PHOTOGRAPHS

As we lift these photographs, we discover the small world we have entered, and we see the intensity of the world before.

*   *   *

She could dance before any of us were born. She could walk for miles. Her legs and her fingers were straight and her shoulders were square and there was no pain in her smiling.

She danced with Jimmy Freel and Pat Flannery at St Wilfred's church hall in Gateshead, with handsome John McGuire at St Dominic's in Byker. She danced at Jessie's Ballroom above the Co-op in Hebburn and at the Oxford in Newcastle. As a child she wore boots with studs hammered into the soles by her father. She ran down Felling Bank to school in them each morning and strode back up again each afternoon. She walked to Lasky's farm by the

Heather Hills for bacon. As a young woman she walked in the Pennines with Joan around Alston. She camped with brothers and cousins in fields behind pubs in Northumberland. She walked home in dancing shoes through the blackout from Newcastle. At the war's end she and Dad took rooms at the Lodore Hotel by Derwent Water. She walked with him every morning over Cat Bells' summit and around the lake. They honeymooned at the Swan in Grasmere and they walked for hours each day, feasting on milk and sandwiches given in the remotest farmhouses on the highest fells.

These things are true. We know this because of the stories we are told, because of the photographs we see.

*   *   *

Arthritis is as secret as the soul. No way of knowing when it starts. Is it present in this wedding photograph, in this straight smiling woman who calmly grips the arm of this straight proud man? In this woman who perches on

185

the five-bar gate above Alston, she in the knee-length skirt, with her ankles comfortably crossed, with the wind playing in her hair? In this skinny-legged girl in loose frock and heavy boots who stands in the back garden in Rectory Road? Did it enter her, one secret and indecipherable moment, slipping into her like breath? Or was it always in her, conceived with her and entering the world with her, a familiar, a hidden companion, a malevolent twin? She had no answers. She told us there had been twinges in her shoulder as she sat at her desk in Elders Walker, stiffness in her fingers as she pressed the typewriter keys. And earlier? She couldn't know. How could she have compared the pains of childhood play with the pains of her friends? How could she suspect a specialness in the ache she felt after dancing or on coming down from a fell? Speculation was pointless. She shrugged her twisted shoulders, turned up her crooked hands, clicked her tongue, pondered on the photographs and smiled and smiled. How could she have imagined

186

that this was how she was intended to be?

*   *   *

We are photographs ourselves. Her image is upon us.

As I grew, I was stopped many times in the streets by strangers. They saw the shape of her face in mine.

'You're Kathleen's son,' they said. They smiled and their voices softened. 'You should have seen her, boy.'

They reached out to me, held me for an instant: she was so lovely, she was the best of dancers, she was so filled with life.

'Tell her I was asking,' they said. 'She'll remember me.'

This happened to all of us, so many times.

It happens still when I return, even now, after she's been dead these years. I walk through Felling Square, or raise a drink in the Columba. I see the eyes watching, see them softening.

I wait for the gentle touch on my shoulder.

I wait for the familiar words,
'You're Kathleen's son . . .'

I wait for time to dissolve, for the stories to begin, for her unspoiled image to be exposed again.

LOOSA FINE

She couldn't say her name, Louisa, so we copied her and called her Loosa. Loosa Fine. She lived with her mother in Coniston in the shade of the bypass by the old coal line. They'd been abandoned by her father years ago. She sat on the low wall of her front garden, eating bread and jam, fiddling with the hem of her skirt. She waved and giggled as we passed. The kindly reached out to touch her cheek or her shoulder.

'I is Loosa,' she would say. 'You has speaken to me. You has speaken to Loosa Fine.'

I first came upon her soon after we had moved to Thirlmere. I was walking back from the butcher's with some soup bones. She lay jerking and squirming on the pavement in Rydal. Froth was seeping from her mouth. A neighbour had folded his coat and pushed it beneath her head. Nothing else we could do, he told me. A matter of letting it work its way through her. Other kids came and we stood around to watch her struggling all alone. The neighbour sent me for Mrs Fine and I banged on the door and yelled for her. There was dirt and litter in the hallway, darkness inside the house, the scent of cigarettes and urine. 'Where's she this time?' she muttered as she lumbered out and shoved me back on to the path.

James Bridon lived two doors down the street from her. He told us of Loosa dancing in the back garden at night, of her howling like a wolf at the moon. One dusk I gave him some cigarettes to let me stand with him at his bedroom window and watch for her. She came out at last and roamed through the waist-high grass and weeds. We edged the window open and heard her muttering and gurgling. 'What's she saying?' I asked. He shook his head. She caught us watching and she pointed and laughed at us. Her attention was drawn away from us, to the bats that had come out to fly over the gardens and the line beyond. She followed them with quick lurching movements of her head. We shut the window tight, soon full darkness came and there was nothing else to see or hear.

Each morning a green trip bus came to Coniston to take Loosa away. It came slowly, grinding its gears, filling the narrow roadways of the estate. The kids inside gazed out on us with empty eyes. Some showed their tongues to us, giggled, let their heads loll against the windows. Our parents told us not to stare but we couldn't help ourselves.

'What happened to her?' we asked.

'There but for the grace of God,' they said. 'His workings are mysterious, but there will be some purpose to it. Each child is precious in His eyes.'

They used Loosa as our guide. They clicked their tongues when we complained of little pains or minor problems. 'Think of Loosa,' they said. 'Just think of poor Loosa Fine.'

It was soon after Loosa left school that James told us about the older boys. He believed they came over the line from Wardley, or came down the line all the way from Springwell. He said she went with them into the tunnel where the line ran beneath the bypass. This was before the line was cindered and signposted as it is today. Dense weeds and bramble grew over the rusting rails, the sleepers, the runners for the cable that had once hauled wagons up and down between the river and the pit at Felling's summit. He said he'd seen boys taking turns to go in to her. 'What about her mother?' we asked. He laughed. 'Plastered,' he said. We couldn't believe all this. But soon I realised that our parents' manner when they spoke of Loosa was changing.

'Keep away from her,' they told us. 'Don't look. Stay away from Loosa Fine.'

*   *   *

The older boys weren't mentioned when the talk of sending her to Lourdes started. Each year the pilgrims from our parish took one like Loosa, less fortunate than ourselves and more in need of Our Lady's care. The Lourdes Offerings were collected in a black box on the wall of St Patrick's and each Sunday it rattled with pennies, shillings, half crowns. Each spring Father O'Mahoney listened to the suggestions of his parishioners and prayed for guidance. This year the appeals for Loosa were irresistible. I was with James, kicking a ball on the verges, when the priest came in his Ford Anglia to Coniston. 'On me head, boys!' he called, shaping as if to throw himself for an attempt at goal, before he winked at us, composed himself, and went in to call on Mrs Fine.

*　　　*　　　*

It was the time of the great pilgrimages. To those like me who had never been, Lourdes seemed to be both out of the world and a simple extension of our parish, some warmer and brighter suburb of Tyneside. It was a place of miracles populated by people like ourselves and filled with familiar landmarks. We had images of Our Lady and St Bernadette on our mantelpieces, walls and windowsills.

We sipped Lourdes water along with our medicines, we rubbed it on our aches and pains. Our girls were called Mary, Marie, Maria, Bernadette. We had foot-long photographs showing our pilgrims there. They wore white blouses and socks and carried folded jerkins on their arms. They carried shoulder bags filled with prayer cards and souvenirs. The men wore their white collars outside their dark lapels. Our priests at the front were proud and proprietorial. The Knights of St Columba held the diocesan banner. The names of our parishes were borne on little flags. The faces of our relatives and friends and neighbours smiled out at us through brilliant light.

I knew many who had been and who had prayed for me there. They lived in little hotels with dining rooms that doubled up as prayer rooms. They drank French coffee and ate French bread and tried French wine and beer. They were nostalgic for toast and Scottish and Newcastle ales. They ate roast dinners and complained of the awful tea and the undertaste of garlic that was in everything. They talked of the glorious basilica, the joy and beauty of torchlit processions, the endless gushing of holy water from taps and fountains, the sound of the rosary swelling into the Pyrenean night. They told us of the icy baths and the miracles that had occurred in them, of the crutches of the cured hanging in the grotto. They came back with suntanned faces, carrying bottles of duty-free Teachers and boxes of Player's. In their cases they had painted plaster statues of the beautiful Virgin and kneeling Bernadette, musical grottoes, models of the basilica in snowstorm paperweights, 3D postcards of Bernadette's vision. They brought supplies of the precious water: Virgin-shaped bottles of it, wine flagons of it, tiny pocket-size phials of it. There was never a miracle among our pilgrims, but they knew that they had been healed inside. They came home bearing their gifts as if from some great adventure or as if waking from some astounding dream.

*　　　*　　　*

It was a Saturday afternoon in early summer when Loosa's pilgrimage departed. I stood in the garden with my mother watching the sky until an aeroplane heading south passed over us. We waved and giggled, knowing that the pilgrims would be looking down upon Tyneside and seeing no one, but waving, too.

'Will Loosa get cured?' I asked her.

She laughed and said, 'We are all in God's hands.'

'Why is God so mysterious?'

'He does give signs.'

'Like Lourdes?'

'Yes. Like Lourdes.'

We watched the aeroplane disappear. I walked out of the garden into the quiet estate. I called for James but there was no answer. I sat on the bypass embankment. Traffic whined above and behind me. I looked up into the empty sky and down upon the overgrown coal line and the pale pebble-dashed homes. I said a prayer for Loosa and the others. I sat waiting.

*   *   *

I knew many of the other pilgrims that year. They included my Uncle Michael from St Wilfred's; a girl from my class named Claire Gullane; and Mrs Worley, an old woman from Ennerdale whose errands I used to run. I imagined them with their candles in the fervent crowds. I pictured Uncle Michael swigging great glasses of wine and conducting choruses of 'O Sacred Heart' and 'Cushy Butterfield' in the hotel bar. I saw Mrs Worley trembling as she lifted the water to her lips, beating her heart as she whispered prayers for her long-gone husband. I saw Claire copying the ardent posture of Bernadette as she knelt at the grotto. I imagined them caring for Loosa, taking her arm, directing her attention to Our Lady, teaching the prayers to her. In the middle of the second week a card from Uncle Michael Came, sent on the day they'd arrived. He wrote of the clean hotel, the crystal mountain air, the holiness you felt as soon as you stepped out of the aeroplane. He promised he would pray for us. I asked when we'd be able to go and my father said I was right, we'd have to make the effort soon. He laughed and told me that in the meantime Felling would have to do.

The days were lengthening. I spent hours after school with James on the abandoned line, shinning up into hawthorn trees and searching for eggs. We blew out the insides and rested them on sand in shoeboxes. We shone torches into the roof of the tunnel, threw sticks at the bats there, getting them to fly out early. We saw obscene pictures of Loosa chalked on the walls, lurid statements of what she'd done. We fought with the Wardley boys, swore at them through the hawthorn and bramble, threw rocks at them. We saw groups of boys roving higher up the line but we knew of the wildness of those from Springwell, and we kept away. We looked through the back fence and the weeds towards Mrs Fine inside her house, saw her at the kitchen table shoving great forkfuls of food into her mouth, saw beer bottles lined up on the windowsill. 'Just imagine,' we whispered. 'Poor Loosa Fine.' When we climbed back into the estate I touched the Sacred Heart medal on my breast and asked to be forgiven for my transgressions. When I slept, I dreamt of Our Lady with her hands held out in comfort, descending from the sky towards the estate.

*   *   *

They returned on a Saturday night. After Sunday Mass at St Patrick's we heard the first of the stories. All the first day and all through the first night Loosa had howled for her mother. A French doctor sedated her. The Felling pilgrims took turns in sitting with her in her room. She wouldn't eat, wouldn't drink, muttered gibberish and obscenities. A group of nuns and priests came for her, carried her to the Virgin, held her at the grotto, prayed passionately for her. She began to howl again and attack her helpers when they laid her in the baths. A girl called

199

Doreen McKenna from a Gateshead parish stepped forward and somehow managed to calm her. She was again sedated, again taken to her room. Doreen sat with her while the pilgrims gathered in the dining room to say the Rosary and the Memorare and sing 'O Queen of Heaven Come'. On the third day Doreen fed her with milk and bread and she was taken out again, now more subdued because of her excesses. Doreen held her arm as they joined a procession. On the steps of the basilica Loosa fell down and entered a fit. A space was cleared around her. She came out of it and showed by her actions that she wished to continue. At the grotto she fell again and lay as if in violent agony below Our Lady. After a time she raised her head to those gathered anxiously around her. Doreen knelt at her side, whispering gently to her. Loosa muttered and gurgled, until at last her words were understood.

Her has speaken,' said Loosa. 'My lady has speaken to me.'

Those who were telling us paused and watched our faces.

'Our Lady,' my mother whispered.

'Yes. So it seemed. Our Lady appeared, and spoke to Loosa Fine.'

I waited. The adults around me moved into a closer group and lowered their voices. A neighbour looked down at me, asked me not to listen. My mother told me to be good. I saw Claire on her own behind a crowd of her relatives. I went to her and asked her to tell me about Loosa. She bit her lip and was wide-eyed and beaming.

'She saw Our Lady,' she said.

'What else?'

'Our Lady spoke to her. It was a miracle.'

'What else, though?'

'Our Lady told her secrets.'

'What secrets?'

'Secrets she can't tell.'

She bit her lip again.

'A miracle,' she said.

'Who's Doreen?'

'Somebody from Gateshead. Loosa's friend. Her helper. She appeared like an angel at Loosa's side.'

On the way home from church in the car I asked my parents if it was true.

My father said it depended what I meant by true.

'That she saw Our Lady,' I said.

'Who can tell?'

'Our Lady told Loosa secrets.'

'So it's said.'

'That's what she did at Fatima. Told the children secrets.'

'That's true.'

We turned off the bypass and went into the estate. I looked at the pebble-dashed houses, the little gardens. I thought of Loosa and her poverty and her awful mother. I recalled her lying gurgling and out of control on the pavement in Rydal.

'I think I believe it,' I said.

'You must remember Loosa's a sick girl,' said my mother. 'She's almost a woman but she'll always be a little child.'

'I know,' I said. 'That's what saints are like.'

In the afternoon I went to see if there was anything Mrs Worley needed. Peace of mind, she said. She gave me a prayer card and a tiny phial of water. Enough for three colds and two doses of the runs, she said. I asked how Loosa had been. She looked at me and pursed her lips.

'Little madams,' she said.

She kept watching me.

'You just keep away from Loosa Fine, lad.'

Later I crouched with James on the line. We saw Loosa and her mother and another in the house. 'Doreen,' I whispered. She was tall and blonde. She kept coming to the window, looking out. We kept ducking down. Then we saw Father O'Mahoney with them, and we heard Loosa's mother yelling. He came outside with her, into the garden. He held her arm and his voice was firm but sympathetic. We heard him telling her that Loosa needed help, that he could help to arrange it. Loosa's mother shoved him away. She spat into the weeds.

'Damn priests!' she yelled. 'Damn church! Get back to Hell!'

Doreen stayed. We watched them all at the table together. When we went back into the estate, we saw the little bunch of kids sitting on the front wall and looking in, adults in their gardens watching from a distance.

*   *   *

At school next day it was said that Loosa had a total of seven visions. Our Lady had given her the dates of the next war and of the end of the world. She had given her a message that could only be repeated to the Pope. Doreen had been chosen as her interpreter in this task. Loosa had been told that she had borne her troubles with great strength and that a place at God's side was reserved for her in Heaven. Claire was asked if this was correct and she beamed and said it must be. She had seen a miracle, she told us. She had been in Lourdes with a saint.

It was Anthony O'Dowd who said the visions had come from Hell. His grandmother had been there. He said that as Loosa lay on the basilica steps his grandmother had sensed a dark angel hovering above them all. She had stepped back as the others leaned forward. There had been a scent of sulphur and a shadow had fallen over Lourdes.

'It's true,' he said.

'It's not,' said Claire.

'It is. Loosa was ensnared by the Devil. From then onward she spent her time consorting with his demons.'

We looked at Claire. She was crying. Anthony stepped towards her and pointed at her.

'And that Doreen?' he said. 'She's a black blasted bitch from Hell if ever there was one!'

*   *   *

Uncle Michael visited that week. He brought water and cigarettes and whisky. He sang 'Bobby Shaftoe' in French for us. He asked if I was courting yet and told me of the lovely girls of France. He winked and said they'd spirit my heart away.

My mother asked him what the truth was about Loosa Fine.

'I saw one girl fall and another girl help her up.'

'And is it true what they say she

said?'

'Yes. I heard her. She said that Our Lady had spoken.'

'Her has speaken to me,' I said.

'That's right. And her has speaken God knows me and loves me. Her has speaken I will guard you always, Loosa Fine. Poor girl. She was ill and exhausted. She was kneeling at the grotto like a crazed thing. Her has speaken secret things, she said.'

'And did you believe it?' I said.

He sipped his whisky.

'I saw nothing but the girl. I heard nothing but what she said. We waited for a sign. We prayed for a sign, but there was nothing.' He shrugged. 'Who can tell?'

He and my father drank again. My mother looked at the clock and then at me. I turned my eyes away and listened to them talk of miracles, how they were so difficult to believe, how they might be caused by a kind of madness, how they could be the tricks of the Devil rather than the works of God.

'This could be true of so much that we believe,' my father said.

Uncle Michael nodded and drank.

'Aye,' he said. 'We live in darkness.'

They drank more whisky.

'In the deep deep deepest dark,' they said.

They giggled.

My mother eyed me again.

Uncle Michael reached out and touched my cheek. 'Let all boys be assumed into their beds,' he said. He leaned over and kissed my brow.

Later I lay down and pressed my ear to the floor but could hear nothing of sense. The voices were muffled and mysterious. Uncle Michael told a long tale while my parents laughed and questioned and exclaimed. I heard how the men's voices were loosened by the drink. I heard the names of Loosa and Doreen repeated many times. There were calls to Jesus and his mother for help. The end of the tale was sombre in its telling, then there was a long silence, then sighs and muttered prayers, then much laughter again as Uncle Michael broke out into a noisy 'Bobby Shaftoe'.

Next day I asked what had been told. Nothing I'd understand, my mother said, but I should pray for Loosa. What she'd been led to had nothing to do with Our Lady. At school Anthony O'Dowd said that after the vision Loosa went back to howling and screaming again. Doreen stayed with her in the hotel. They stopped going to the grotto. One afternoon they were seen with French boys in the outskirts of Lourdes. They were seen walking with them into the woods and vineyards outside. His grandmother herself saw Doreen on a bench with some boys in a park. She saw Doreen arguing in French and laughing with the boys and taking money from them. She saw Loosa in a shrubbery waiting, and the boys going to her one by one. The older pilgrims took over Loosa's care, but Anthony said Doreen had still come home with more money than she'd taken, and had been seen counting a bag full of francs on the plane. That evening James came

208

through the estate to find me. He said the boys from Springwell had started coming back again. Now they were coming through the fence and going into Loosa's house itself. Did I want to watch with him? I gave him three cigarettes and stood at the window with him. I expected nothing, but as the light faded a boy in a green jacket emerged from the tunnel and came to the fence. Doreen appeared for a moment and called him. He pushed through into the garden and kept his head low as he hurried in. 'See?' whispered James. I touched the Sacred Heart medal at my breast. We saw the boy leave in the deepening darkness. 'Jesus,' I whispered. 'Jesus Christ.'

*   *   *

We saw Father O'Mahoney come again to Loosa's door. Loosa's mother stood with her hands on her hips in the doorway and yelled at him again. 'Damn priests! Get back to Hell!' The kids on the front wall giggled. The adults in the gardens grinned. The priest tipped his head to us and called, 'All right now, boys?' as he slipped back into his Ford Anglia and drove too quickly away.

Outside St Patrick's that Sunday it was said that Loosa should be taken from her mother and separated from Doreen. She should live with nuns like Bernadette. Only then could her saintliness be nourished and her sinfulness subdued. Some whispered there'd be no point to this: Loosa with her clumsy body and tangled mind was beyond our help. All we could offer were our prayers that God in his mysterious manner might look kindly upon his troubled child. Uncle Michael and my father continued to discuss the complexities of faith. 'Could it be,' asked Uncle Michael, 'that Loosa is sent to show that evil might be as innocent as goodness?'

In the afternoon I climbed on to the line. I moved slowly, stepping from sleeper to sleeper through the tall weeds and grasses. There were fledglings cheeping in the hawthorn. I closed my eyes, felt the sun, imagined this place as warm and bright as France. When I opened them I saw Loosa in her garden turning slow circles and staring up into the blue. I waded towards her and stood close to her fence. She saw me and started to giggle.

'Loosa,' I said. 'What did she say?'

She blinked and gulped and licked her lips.

'What did she say, Loosa?'

She tilted her head back and giggled at the sky.

'What were the secrets, Loosa?'

She fiddled with the hem of her skirt.

'What did she speaken?' I asked.

'Her did speaken I is good. Her did speaken I is lovely Loosa Fine.'

'What else, Loosa?'

Loosa's head rocked and her eyes blinked.

'What were the secrets, Loosa?'

Behind her I saw Doreen coming out of the house. She stood at Loosa's side and smiled at me. She wore a blouse the colour of Our Lady's vestments. Her hair was held back by a golden Alice band. She put her arm around

Loosa's shoulder.

'Who's this?' she asked.

'Him has speaken to me.'

'Shall we ask him to come inside?'

Loosa giggled. Doreen gazed at me.

I said nothing. There was no one on the line. I looked up at James' window and saw no one.

'Shall we?' said Doreen.

Doreen's lips were red and shining in the light.

'Well?' she said.

I could see right through the house: Loosa's mother inside, the pebble-dashed houses beyond, the children playing on the verges.

'Well?' said Doreen. She winked, and pointed to the breach in the fence.

I touched the Sacred Heart.

'What did Our Lady say?' I asked.

Doreen grinned. She licked her lips.

'Her did speaken Loosa Fine is lovely,' she said.

Through the house I saw Mrs Worley passing slowly by. I touched the Sacred Heart again and turned away.

I went into the tunnel and threw stories at the bats and watched them flee into the light.

*   *   *

The next weekend a police car came. James ran through the estate to get me. A crowd had already gathered outside Loosa's house. We could see the great silhouettes of the two policemen inside. Their blue and white car gleamed in the roadway. The house was closed but we could hear the screaming of Mrs Fine. Soon the door opened and the policemen came out with Doreen. She had a carrier bag with some clothes stuffed into it. She was smoking a cigarette and she looked at us all with scorn. Somebody shouted that they'd seen the Virgin Doreen and the kids screamed with laughter. Mrs Fine yelled that all of us could get back to Hell. The policemen were awkward and embarrassed and there were big patches of sweat on their pale blue shirts. Doreen caught my eye for a moment and licked her lips as they drove her away.

'What's that all for?' I asked James,

and he shrugged.

'What's that for?' I asked my father who'd come to the back of the crowd.

'Leading into temptation,' he said.

We watched the crowd disperse. We saw Loosa come to the window and we could see that she was crying.

'Poor soul,' said my father.

We walked back together through the estate. The place was dry and bleached in the sun's glare. The kids behind us went on screaming. I fingered the phial of water that Mrs Worley had given me. I closed my eyes and imagined seeing through Loosa's eyes, hearing through her ears.

'Could there be visions here?' I asked.

'Who knows what we might see? Who knows what might be shown to us?'

*   *   *

Nothing was done to Doreen. She was warned to keep away from Felling and from Loosa. We heard that she'd lost her faith, that she told her priest in the middle of Mass he was a hypocrite, that her family had always been a wild bunch, that she could be seen on Saturday nights wandering in Pink Lane in Newcastle. Loosa went back to sitting on the front wall of her garden, eating bread and jam in the heat, telling those who passed that she had been speaken to, that she was lovely Loosa Fine. The kindly reached out in compassion to touch her cheek or her shoulder. I watched her, tried to imagine the secrets that were lost in her. In church the faithful prayed for her and wondered what might be done for her. And then we saw her belly growing, and knew of the new life inside Loosa Fine.

*   *   *

It was late one Friday and the sun was huge and red above the bypass when Mrs Fine let Father O'Mahoney in. He brought two women from the Legion of Mary with him. James and I watched from the line as the adults talked at the kitchen table. Loosa gazed from the

215

window into the burning sky.

'Wonder who it was,' I said.

'Some Frenchie. Some Springweller. Nobody'll ever know.'

'Would you have done it?' I whispered.

James shrugged. 'Would you?'

The priest and the women left alone, but they soon returned and this time Mrs Fine waved from the door as they took Loosa away. She went to Hexham, to the Little Sisters of the Poor. My mother said they were the sweetest and gentlest of all nuns. They would give her the best of care. They would find the best of homes for her little child. They would look after Loosa for ever afterwards.

At St Patrick's we continued to include Loosa in our prayers.

Soon the preparations for next year's pilgrimage were upon us. This time it was decided to send a little boy from Stoneygate named Paul, who'd been born with no eyes.

THE KITCHEN

The drone of the distant city, the clatter and hum of Felling nearby. In another garden, children sing a skipping song: *January, February, March, April, May* . . . An invisible lark high above. A blackbird calling from the apple tree. The scent of roses and warm grass. The sun burns at the centre of the sky. Light pours down into the garden, through the window, through the gap of the half-open door, through dust that seethes, dances, glitters . . .

And Mam smiles.

'Hm. Just look at us. Right out of space again.'

Here she is on the old white chair with a hundred holes like stars. And Dad on the low stool at her side.

'We'd have moved on to a bigger place,' he says.

'I know,' she answers. 'Yes. I know.'

And here we are, leaning against the worktops, the fridge, the sink, the little table. We drink tea and eat toast. We allow the toast to cool for a moment, so that the butter we spread melts only at its edges, so that much of it remains, bright yellow, half-solid on the crisp surface. There is cheese, lemon curd, Golden Shred. So simple, so sweet, enough for all of us.

We breathe so gently, so carefully. We don't stare. The light pours in.

Barbara wears cream trousers, a white blouse, white shoes. Her hair is cut short but it curls around her ears, it curls on her brow. Little silver earrings like teardrops. A narrow silver necklace. She stands with her left hand resting on the bench and her head tilted languidly to one side. She is so shy here, with us all around her. She keeps lowering her eyes, and her face colours gently as she smiles.

I look at Mam and she shakes her head and bites her lip: just give her time. We don't stare. The light doesn't change, the singing goes on. Catherine catches my eye.

'Nothing must happen,' she says. 'Nothing.'

Dad touches Margaret's hand.

'I was thinking,' he says. 'Do you remember? One day you said to me, Where's the smallest place in the world?' She shakes her head.

'I don't remember,' she whispers.

'You were young.'

He smiles at Margaret and at the memory of Margaret and for a moment we all see her as she was and as we were.

'I was thinking, Maybe this is it. Maybe this is the smallest place in the world. Just enough for all of us.'

'What happened?' says Margaret. 'Tell me about the day I asked you and what you said to me.'

'It was nothing much. You were on the floor with your head in the sideboard cupboard. I watched you climbing right inside. What you after? I said. I've lost Nancy in here, you said. The cupboard's too small to be lost in, I said. But she's so small, you said. I found the doll beside me on the settee. Here she is! I said. You ticked her off. Who said you could go off wandering all alone? you said. You came and sat

219

on my knee and we looked at the open sideboard door and the dark cupboard. Could I have got lost in there? you said. Too small, I told you. You'd hardly get *in* it, never mind get lost in it. Look at the size of you and the size of that. We sat quiet for a while. The day was like this. Sun shining, blackbirds singing. After a while, you said, Where's the smallest place in the world? Then you said, What would we find sitting all safe inside?'

'What did you say?' says Margaret.

'Isn't it silly?' He smiles. 'I don't remember. But maybe this is it, this kitchen, and here we are, all sitting safe inside.'

Unchanging light, unchanging song: the lark, the blackbird, the children. The dust seethes and dances in the light. Catherine takes more toast from beneath the grill. We allow it to cool for a moment before putting the butter on.

'This one got lost,' says Mam. 'Went off wandering on her own, the smallest of us all. Who said you could do that, now?'

Barbara blushes and smiles.

'That was the smallest place,' she whispers. 'No room for anybody else but me in there.'

'I know,' says Mam. 'Oh, I know.'

'Thought you'd all forsaken me. Thought you'd all forget me.'

'I wasn't even here when you were here,' says Mary. But I still remember you. I still don't forget you.'

'I know that now,' says Barbara. 'But I thought I'd be alone for ever. Me so little and all of you so big. And so many of you, more of you even though I was gone. You'd have each other and the little memory of me would just get lost.'

'We never forgot,' says Dad. 'And if we didn't remember true, we just made bits up.'

Barbara laughs.

'Made bits up!'

'Yes. Truth and memories and dreams and bits made up.'

'Bits made up. But bits made up that kept me safe and real in all your hearts.'

We listen to the beating of our

hearts.

Barbara says, 'When I began to understand, I used to come among you. I knew you knew I was there. I knew you knew I was always there.'

'Yes,' says Mam. 'We always knew.'

We smile at her. We listen to the blackbirds, to the children singing.

'Tell us about another day,' says Mary.

'Tell them about another day,' says Dad.

'We were at the beach,' says Mam. She touches Barbara. 'All of us but you. South Shields, another day like this, all burning bright. Dad and I sat by the bandstand and spread the blankets and towels on the grass. Mary and Margaret were on their hunkers at the sea's edge with their buckets, pouring sand into the sea and sea into the sand. Catherine knelt building a castle. The boys were right in, diving and swimming and yelling at the cold. We sat on the warm grass and leaned back on the warm bricks. Dad put a kettle on the primus. We saw the fret coming in. It was white and thick and so sudden. The horizon disappeared, then the great boat that was waiting to enter the Tyne, then the waves. And the fret came closer, until the boys were gone. You remember?'

'I remember,' says Dad. 'I ran down, and I called and called. I ran into the sea. The sea was icy cold and the air was icy cold. I stood there splashing, calling. You remember?'

'Yes,' says Colin. 'We heard you shouting and it was like you were a hundred miles away.'

'I stood up and watched,' says Mam. 'Dad in his soaking trousers, the girls behind him on the shore. I saw Dad running into the fret until he had disappeared, too.'

Dad laughs.

'Blundered into them, knocked them flying, tumbled into the sea myself. We came out icy cold and soaking wet.'

'Giggling and splashing,' says Mam. 'You all came up to me, to the bandstand, the tea, the sandwiches. Soon everybody wrapped in towels. You'll catch your deaths, I said. You will. You'll catch your deaths.'

We drink tea, nibble toast, try to remember.

'It was me that saw her,' says Catherine. 'The little girl standing in the fret, pale as the mist, knee-deep in the sea. I pointed. There! I said. There! We watched the fret, going back as quickly as it had come in. In the water, I said. There, in the fret. There. Peel your eyes. I ran down to the sea, pointing. There! The fret went back, the sea was empty, just water, little waves. Not a soul in there. Dreamed it night after night. Little girl in the water. The missing one, the one who seemed always to be somewhere in the fringes. Catch her in the corner of your eye, then turn your head and she'd be gone.'

We turn our eyes to Barbara. She turns her eyes to each of us, eyes shining like the sea, complexion pale as sea fret. 'I didn't make you up,' says Catherine.

'No,' says Barbara, and she reaches out and touches Catherine's cheek. 'And it doesn't matter exactly what's true and what's made up. I was always there. I am always there, despite my death.'

We are silent at the word, but we sigh together, those of us who are in life and those of us who are in death.

'What's death?' says Mary suddenly. Mary looks at Mam, at Dad, at Barbara. 'You all died. What's death?'

'Death is very big and very frightening,' says Barbara. 'Death is being all alone and waiting for others to come to you.'

'Death is separation,' says Dad. 'It's when you're torn away from those who have hardly known you, and who will have trouble in remembering you.' He touches Mary on the cheek. 'Like you and Margaret,' he says. 'You would always have difficulty in remembering me.'

'Death is knowing you're about to die,' says Mam. 'It's seeing the dead and seeing the living all at once. It's wanting not to die and not to live. It's wanting to stay with the last breath when the dead and the living are all around you, and touching you, and whispering, It's all right, Mam.

Everything's all right. But there's no way of staying with the last breath. You have to die.'

'And then?' says Colin. 'What happens then?'

Barbara smiles.

'And then the dead get together and tell stories about the living, just as the living tell stories about the dead.'

'Yes,' says Dad. 'The dead begin with, Do you remember? or, Let me tell you about the time, or, There was once . . .'

We're silent again. We listen to the birds, the children singing outside.

Mam laughs.

'I sang that,' she says. *'January, February, March, April* . . . Jumping the rope, running round to the line again. Time and again and time and again and time and again. There was once a little girl with lovely leaping legs . . .'

She hums the relentless tune and taps her toes on the floor. 'And anyway,' she says. 'As well as life and death, there's this.'

'What's this?' says Mary.

'The kitchen. Just the kitchen, I

226

suppose.'

'The smallest place in the world,' says Dad. 'An impossible place. An impossible story. A kind of Heaven.'

'And what's Heaven?' says Colin.

'Maybe it's just this, an impossible afternoon when everyone is together all at once.'

We gaze out at the light, through the seething dust. The sun still hangs at the dead centre of the sky. The children and the blackbird sing. No one speaks. Nothing happens. We look at each other, touch each other.

'Tell us a story,' says Margaret.

'Tell us a story,' we say.

'There was once . . .' says Mam.

We look at her.

'Yes,' she whispers. 'Listen. This is true . . . Hm. There was once a little boy from Carlisle Street who lost his voice in the winter snow. You remember?'

'I remember,' says Dad.

'His name was Jack Law,' says Mam. 'He had seven sisters, a loving mammy and a loving daddy, and nowt but sacking tied around his feet . . .'

We listen to the truth, the memories, the bits made up. We gaze at each other. We eat warm buttered toast. We know that the sun will fall, that the children and the birds will be silent. We know that we will return to separate lives and separate deaths. We listen to the stories, that for an impossible afternoon hold back the coming dark.

JACK LAW

'Let me tell you about Jack Law,' whispered Carmel Bright.

We were in Dragone's. My grandmother was at my side. Came faced us across the thin table. They shared a pot of tea: two cups, the teapot, a jug of steaming water. Jack himself was in the next cubicle, past Carmel. Like me, he held a heavy Horlicks cup between his hands. Sometimes he raised his head and stared through the dividing glass, but there was nothing in his eyes.

I leaned on my grandmother. I watched him, his wild long hair, ancient clothes, filthy fingers on the pale cup. Jack Law. I'd seen him always, rope around his waist, kitbag at his back, striding endlessly through our town.

'Who is Jack Law?' I whispered.

My grandmother shook her head, pressed a finger to her lips: not kind to talk of him, not with him so close.

'Maybe there is a kindness in it,' said

Carmel.

She sighed, as if she felt Jack Law's gaze upon her back. Her green eyes softened as she leaned across.

'It'll be all right. Drink your drink and let me tell you about Jack Law.'

I sipped the Horlicks. I remembered the first time I ever saw him, striding past our garden in the sleet. I remembered tugging at the hand that held me: Who's that? Who's that?

'It happened so long ago I can't even be sure it happened as I say it did. Stories change in the telling, memory makes up as much as it knows. We were very small. The things we saw were all mixed up with the things we dreamed and the things that we were scared of. We were at school together: me, your Grandma, Jack Law, lots of others that you know and lots that's dead and gone. Forty-five of us, fifty, who's to know? Too many. No way of teaching anything worth having, not when there's half a hundred of you and just one man before you with a stick. Filled your head with things that wouldn't stop, things that still won't

230

stop once you let them go. Many's the night I'm in my cold bed and if I'm not careful here they come from all those years ago. Seven sevens are forty-nine, eight sevens are fifty-six, I, said the sparrow, with my bow and arrow, Infant Jesus meek and mild, January, February, March, April, I believe in God, the Father Almighty, Maker of heaven and earth, a for apple, b for ball, c for cat . . . You know, Esther? Yes, you know. From all those years back, things we learned, useless things just going round and round and round our heads.'

She smiled and touched my brow.

'Not like now, though. Thinking's happening in there. You won't fall for it.'

She loosened the silken scarf at her throat. I sipped the Horlicks. Jack wiped his ragged sleeve across his red lips.

'We had Mr Marks, a good man, no abuser of his stick, least no more than most were then. Beat the rhythms on his desk with it, whipped the latecomers and the chatterers and the sniggerers with it. But never touched the ones that were just slow. Never touched Jack Law.

'You know your Catechism, boy? Course you do. The hammering at it still goes on. Who made you? Why did He make you? In whose image did He make you? Course you know. They're the easy ones, the early ones. You know the other ones, the ones that's deep inside the book? What were the chief sufferings of Christ? What is Hope? How can we show that the Angels and Saints know what passes on earth? In how many ways can we cause or share the guilt of another's sin? Why are we . . . Never mind, don't answer me, don't try to think of the answers. Let them go. Every morning, nine till half past nine, we had the Catechism: Mr Marks chanting the question, half a hundred chanting the answer back. Each of us with the little book to take home in our pockets, the only book they ever gave. Learn it in school and learn it at the fireside till you couldn't forget it no matter how hard you later tried. Unless you were Jack Law, and others like Jack Law.

'We had a headmistress, Miss Sloane. Remember, Esther? Not like these you're getting now, these pretty things with legs and brains. Big as the door to our eyes when she came into Mr Marks's room. Hard as stone. Bundled up in scratchy tweeds. Face you didn't want to see. Face that kept repeating and repeating in your dreams. Remember, Esther? Esther Conroy, Who made you? Carmel Bright, Why did God make you? Jack Law, In whose image did God make you?'

She poured more water into the teapot, poured more tea into her own and my grandmother's cup. Jack Law stared down into his rich sweet Horlicks.

'Jack was a pretty little scrawny little thing. Eyes like saucers and bones like twigs. Lived on Carlisle Street just outside the school. One of eight or nine, who knows? One of lots of them. Dad worked on the river, humping coal from coal trucks on to coal boats. Mam took in washing. She chopped sticks and sold them round the streets. She sold sweets from her front window: barley twists, cinnamon sticks, liquorice roots. You know those things? Kids everywhere inside, all neglect but bright as buttons mainly. Sisters sitting there with Jack and helping him. Who made you, Jack? Why did God make you, Jack? Sisters filled with love, holding their little brother tight. In whose image did God make you, Jack? Doesn't matter, Jack. You know God made you. You know God made you to know Him, love Him and serve Him in this world and to be happy with Him for ever in the next. Long as you know that, what's there to worry about? Maybe when he cried they told him, God made you in His own image and likeness, Jack, but it was just to comfort him. They knew he'd never remember more than two.'

She paused and smiled.

'You're watching Jack. You're wondering does he hear, does he understand. You're wondering like your Grandma, is this hurting Jack. Who's to know? Ask him and there'd be no answer. The faith drives some to drink and some to silence. You could drive a nail in that man's hand and never get a yelp. What's certain is there were those that loved him then and there's those that love him still.'

She allowed her voice to rise.

'There's many still alive that love Jack Law.'

There was no change visible in his face. He raised his cup and drank. He wiped his ragged sleeve across his mouth.

'Fridays were the best days and the worst days. Story day. Used to love it, listening to Mr Marks as he read them from the book. Noah and his ark. Jonah in the whale. Little David. Hairy Esau. Abraham and Isaac climbing up the mountain. Loved writing them. Not the way I hear you're let to do them now from your imagination and your dreams. We copied the lines on to the slates then copied the writing on the lines, and better keep it neat and straight, eh, Esther? Else it's the rap on the slate and Mr Marks all sharp and saying, Get it done again! Jesus walking on the water. Jesus changing water into wine. Jesus walking round his world, curing and healing and taking pity as he went. Yes, all those lovely tales. And in among them all the knowledge that Miss Sloane would soon be in to test us. Who made you? Why did God make you? Standing there huge before us, pointing down to pale scared faces, lining up in the front of the class the ones that didn't know. How could they not? I couldn't understand it till I found myself out there with my hand stretched out and Miss Sloane in front of me with Mr Marks's stick. Dread makes fools of all of us. You found that yet?'

She shook her head.

'Don't answer me. Put the question from your head. He's still there? Silent Jack's still with us?'

I nodded. He'd finished his drink. He gazed down at his clasped hands. I leaned on my grandmother again, felt her shifting to allow me in.

Most every Friday, Jack was there, of course. More than any other, Jack was there. You make Jesus weep, she told him. You make his Holy Mother wring her hands in fear for you. Where you going to end, Jack Law? It was the question that he'd learned to answer. In Hell, Miss Sloane. That's right, in Hell, she said, and she whipped him all the more.

'They were poor days. Poverty you wouldn't credit now. Folk going round in rags. Just the luckiest kids with boots on their feet and warm coats on their backs. The ones like Jack Law coming into school with thrice-time-holey hand-me-downs and sometimes nowt but sacking taped around their feet. Come winter, Mr Marks'd load the classroom fire up and make sure the ones in peril were in its shine. He was a good man but a weak man. When Miss Sloane came in that Friday with the devil in her eyes he should have stood in front of us and protected us, but he backed down, and let her have her way.

'Jack Law was nearest the fire. She whipped the stick down on to his slate. Practising for Judgement Day, Jack Law? In whose image did God make you, Jack Law? His mouth gagged and gaped and nowt came out. She whipped the slate again and asked the question again. I know, Miss, calls one of Jack's sisters from the back of the class. Me too, says another. Miss Sloane glares across at them and there's only silence.

'Outside it's winter, the yard's all ice. There's been earlier snow that's hard as stone with slides and games. Now the snow's come back, tumbling past the windows, swirling down on to the ice. She stands there watching it. She calls Jack Law and puts a Catechism in his hand. You will learn the answer at last, Jack Law. Go out into the yard. Stand there at the centre where I can see you. Take the book. Read it until you remember. Mr Marks is gasping. He's there with a coat in his hand, someone's coat, anyone's. She closes her eyes and shakes her head. No, thank you, Mr Marks. No need for that. Off you go, Jack Law. And out he goes, in his thin rags and his sacking and he doesn't look back.

'Please, miss! Oh, please, Miss Sloane! Weeping sisters and weeping

238

girls. Children craning to the window, seeking to see out through the snow. Don't speak! she yells. Don't move! She stands there at the window watching. She sighs and turns back to us. The little pains we make you suffer now will give you due warning of the eternity of pain to be found in Hell. Carmel Bright, Who made you? Esther Conroy, Why did God make you? When she's asked enough and whipped enough, she turns to Mr Marks. One hour should suffice, Mr Marks. Bring him in when an hour's over and we'll try again. And she leaves us.

'We dash to the window. No stopping us. There he is shaking in the centre with the snow tumbling all around. Please, sir! Oh, please, sir, Mr Marks. Oh Mr Marks, so weak and trembling. And as we watch, little Jack starts running out there in the yard, running round and round and round with the Catechism in his hand through the falling snow. Bring him in, we whisper. Please, sir, Mr Marks. Would it happen now? Would no one make a move and run out there and bring him in, no matter what the teachers said or did? Would his brothers not raise their fists and fight to get him back? Would even his sisters just stand weeping going, Please sir, Mr Marks. Maybe not, but way back then the things we saw were all mixed up with the things we were told to believe. The things we knew were wrong were all mixed up with the things we were told were right. We looked down from the window. What we saw and what we knew was little Jack Law running through the icy snow to keep himself out of blazing Hell.

'It came to an end, and maybe the hour wasn't even all used up. Mr Marks went out. He brought him in, purple hands, deathly cheeks, icy water streaming from him. Now we wrapped him in our coats and held him at the fire and we cried and cried. Then came Miss Sloane, looming through the doorway. Well? she says. Have you learned, Jack Law? In whose image did God make you? We gather around him. We pray as we have never prayed. She asks again. His mouth moves and there's not a sound. Not a gag, not a gurgle. Nothing. Silence.

She reaches for the stick. Can you believe she reaches for the stick? But Mr Marks holds it tight. Half a hundred pairs of eyes, daring her at last. Would we have touched her? Would we have torn her to a thousand pieces as we wished to? Who can tell? She casts her gaze across us. She whispers, Remember the punishments that wait for us all if once we falter. Then she goes.'

Carmel placed her hand around the teapot, testing its heat. She poured in the last of the water. Jack Law raised his head, stared through the glass at me and there was nothing in his eyes.

'Nothing was done. A bonny boy turned mute and nothing was done. No mother came screaming to the classroom, no father came breaking down the doors. But understand: it was a house of love Jack Law came from. Mammy and daddy and sisters and brothers just seeking the best for each other all their days. But when a headmistress and the church and faith

241

and the fear of Hell were involved . . .
They were ignorant days. Poor and
ignorant days.'

I felt my grandmother's breath
against me, her deep sighs.

'The years passed and we grew. Jack
Law did his growing up in silence in
our midst. Miss Sloane asked him
nothing more. Mr Marks tended him in
the classroom and his sisters tended
him at home. Once it was thought that
his silence and his air of sweetness may
be signs of a great soul, and they sent
him for a time to the Christian
Brothers as a servant boy. And the
Brothers sent him back discerning
nothing but an absence in his brain and
a blankness in his soul. And we kept on
growing and we grew away from Mr
Marks and Miss Sloane and the noise
of a half a hundred chanting. And
Jack's brothers left and his sisters
married and his mammy died and his
daddy died and there was nothing to be
done about Jack Law.'

She poured the dregs into her own
and my grandmother's cup. I licked the
edge of my cup, tasted the congealed

sweetness there.

'Nothing?' I said.

'Nothing. And as he grew, the restlessness came into him. There were offers from his sisters that they'd take him in, but more and more he started moving out. You've seen him, walking the streets and lanes. You've seen him, sleeping in bus shelters and in the parks. You've seen him, out in all weathers, in his rags and his silence, driven to walking and running round and round his world.'

She heard him moving, standing up, lifting the kitbag to his back.

'There's many still alive that love Jack Law,' she said.

'Yes,' said my grandmother. 'Many still that love Jack Law.'

I leaned on her.

Jack cast his empty eyes across us and headed out into the street.

Carmel lifted the lid, looked down into the empty teapot, sighed.

'And still he runs, keeping himself out of Hell,' she said. She patted my hand.

'It couldn't happen now. Not now.

Not in these days of enlightenment and loss of faith.'

BUFFALO CAMEL
LLAMA ZEBRA ASS

Inside the roof of the blue tent the zodiac was painted in gold. During the interval we stared upward and Colin showed us all which signs we were. The symbols were faded and flaked, were no brighter than the sawdust in the ring far below. The spangles of the trapeze girl as she swung through the lights had been the brightest things up there. Now she walked sadly before us in a tightly-fastened mac and dusty shoes and sold nuts and Mars bars from a tray balanced at her waist.

Margaret knocked me in the ribs.

'Colin's a lion,' she said. 'Catherine's a goat. You're an ugly bull.'

'I know,' I said. 'That's why there's such a stink in here.'

'But you mustn't believe it,' said Colin. 'It's a pagan thing.' He took out his wallet again and went to the girl and bought chocolate for us all.

'They saw animals and gods in the

stars,' I said. 'They thought the stars showed what would happen and what they should do.'

'And we don't believe that,' said Mary.

'God gave us free will. We choose what to do. We decide whether to be good or to be bad.'

We ate the chocolate and waited for the interval to end. I imagined the girl flying across the roof of the tent towards my outstretched arms. Mary asked how she could be twins when there was only one of her. Margaret said she'd like to be the fish, swimming deep down in the sea with seals and dolphins. Catherine said it was best to be the water-carrier, helping thirsty and worn-out travellers, and anyway you just had to stay what you were born as.

The clowns came on and threw buckets of shredded paper at us. They sawed the trapeze girl in two and pretended to forget how to put her together again. She returned with other girls and they stood on the backs of horses that raced furiously around the ring. Men from Russia in singlets and tights balanced from each other's brows on long silver poles. In the posters there'd been elephants and tigers, but neither of them came. The band played in the end, and animals were brought on as a final entertainment for the children. There was a little buffalo, a camel, a llama, a zebra and an ass. They trotted round and round the ring. A Russian stood at the centre, flicking a long whip at them. Such an odd arrangement, so precisely trained: the muscular wide-horned buffalo; the dusty grunting camel with wobbly hump and gangly legs; the dainty llama with its neck so stiff and its eyes alert; the sprightly synthetic zebra; the poor little damp-eyed ass. From the crowd they drew appreciation, much tender sighing, and of course a little mockery upon themselves.

In the doorway as we filed out from the tent, the trapeze girl in her mac sold models of a monkey who climbed to the top of a ladder and tumbled down again.

'Where were the tigers?' asked Margaret. 'Where were the elephants?'

The girl turned her sad eyes to us.

'They've been poorly,' she said. 'Not well at all.' She shrugged.

'Buy them a monkey,' she said to Colin, but he shook his head, we turned away and entered the field outside.

'It's only a small circus after all,' said Colin.

'Ass, buffalo, camel, llama, zebra,' said Mary. 'Alphabetical order.'

We pondered the truth of this.

So where would the elephant have fitted in?' said Catherine.

'Too big,' said Mary. 'It'd squash the others.'

'In the alphabet, nit.'

'Between camel and llama. And the tiger'd go in after llama and eat them all.'

'Where would you three go?' said Margaret. The goat, the lion and the ugly bull.'

We worked it out, told each other. We positioned many more: porcupines, rhinoceros, spiders, moles. We named an animal for each letter, an alphabet of beasts.

Above us the stars began to appear.

'Did God give the animals their names?' said Mary.

No answer.

'When he made them, he must have said what this one was and this one was.'

Again no answer.

'Are the names we use the same as the names God uses? Does he call the zebra zebra and the camel camel?'

'We can't know,' said Catherine. 'We just can't know.'

We walked on, away from the tent, towards the nearby road where the bus stops were. Already long queues were forming there.

Mary put her index fingers out above her brow and played the buffalo. Margaret lowered her head and grunted and hunched her shoulders, a camel. They trotted gently on before us.

Then came a woman's voice: 'Who's allowing them to do this?'

We stopped and found Marion

MacNabola's mother close behind us. Marion was at her side in a tight blue coat, the monkey toy dangling from her hand.

'Do you know that God gave us eternal souls to separate us from all other creatures?' said Mrs MacNabola.

Mary and Margaret paused and turned.

'Do you know that?'

We nodded.

'And do you know that it is an insult to God if we lower ourselves and imitate the beast?'

No answer.

'You are in charge of these children,' she said. 'You must not allow them to wander into sin.'

Colin looked down and lit a cigarette.

Marion stared wide-eyed at us all from behind her mother.

I could see that Mary and Margaret wanted to laugh.

'You do want to see your Daddy again, don't you?' said Mrs MacNabola.

Mary and Margaret returned to us.

We faced the woman, the circus lights, the dwindling crowd approaching us and passing by.

'Think about it,' she said.

I thought about it. I thought of everything I'd been told, that his pain was over, that he was in Heaven, that he waited for us there. I thought of him and prayed for him each night, as I'd been told to, even as I felt the faith deserting me.

Mrs MacNabola raised her finger.

'He'll be watching you,' she said. 'Think of your eternal souls.'

And she shook her head, walked on, drew her daughter towards the road.

'Pig,' whispered Margaret.

'Cow,' whispered Mary.

We giggled, waited, allowed the woman to get far ahead of us. We searched the sky for the constellations of the zodiac. Colin said that the stars had changed position since the first astrologers had seen the lion, the goat, the bull and all the rest.

'You could make yourself see anything,' said Mary. 'Couldn't you?'

The stars were the spangles of a

costume. The trapeze girl was a great arrangement of points of light against the dark.

'Will we come back again?' said Margaret.

Colin shook his head. No. The circus would travel on.

We moved again across the pale dusty field towards the road.

'Can Daddy see us now?' said Margaret.

Yes, we all assured her.

We went through the fence, stood in the queue beneath the streetlights. Behind us, the summit of the blue tent mingled with the sky.

'What would happen if we called the zebra camel?' said Mary.

We laughed and gave the animals the names of other animals.

'What's a horse?' said Mary.

'A dog,' said Catherine.

'No, a goose.'

'Stop it, Michelle,' I said to Mary.

'Sorry, Simon,' she answered.

A bus came, and the first half of the queue climbed aboard. Mrs MacNabola watched us sternly through the window. Marion played gently with the monkey.

Margaret turned her face up to the light and closed her eyes. Catherine put an arm around her.

'Yes, he can,' she whispered. 'Yes. Yes.'

Soon the next bus came, we climbed aboard.

Catherine Colin Margaret Mary Me.

WHERE YOUR WINGS WERE

For a long time after Barbara died, Mam used to pull my shoulders forward, kiss me, and slip her fingers beneath my shoulder-blades.

'You as well,' she'd whisper. 'Just like Barbara, you as well. This is where your wings were. You left them behind when you came here. But be good, and you'll have them back again, one day.'

Barbara was an angel. One of those that God takes early. She was too good to stay here long. She died in infancy, flew straight into God's arms.

At night I tried to imagine her there. I lay in my bed, closed my eyes, tried to dream of her. I told myself that if I did see her, then it wouldn't be dreaming. It would be real. I whispered her name: 'Barbara. Little sister, little angel. Let me see you again.' But it wasn't to be. With my eyes closed or with my eyes open, all I could see was the darkness spreading all around.

As I grew older, and could feel the goodness leaving me, I tried to pray to Barbara, but the words appeared to go nowhere, and they brought me no comfort. Often I fingered my own shoulder-blades and tried to imagine my wings, tried to imagine the feathers, bones and muscles known only to angels. But my fingers encountered my skin, my flesh, my bone: a simple human shape, nothing more. I searched my memory, tried to remember being there myself, so that I might try harder to return. I retreated, went back and back, remembered further, further, tried to imagine being inside my mother, then the time that preceded being inside my mother. But I could go no further than when I was an infant of two, maybe three, certainly before Barbara came. My first memory was nothing of note, just me sitting in a pushchair staring up at Mam, and Dad at her side. I believe we're in the garden, we've just come through the gate. My parents are so tall, so dark, silhouetted against the blazing sun. I see Mam lean towards me, smiling.

'Look at him,' she says, and I hear their gentle laughter. 'You all right, my little angel?' she asks. I feel her light touch on my cheek, hear the first words I remember, naming me as an angel.

Before that moment, it is as if there's nothing. I do not exist. Trying to go back only emphasises my going forward. I become older. And as a boy, as I grew older, I felt myself heading further and further towards a terrible dark.

It was painful to lie there failing to imagine Barbara, with my parents sleeping in the room next door, and to feel the time of dreams approaching. There seemed to be nothing I could do about these dreams. I didn't want them, I didn't encourage them. I didn't even have to imagine them. They just came out of the night, out of my skull. They came at me, night after night after night.

I confessed the dreams. At church, I knelt in front of the screen and told Father O'Mahoney about them. He was an old man with a gentle Irish voice that never seemed to criticise anything. I knew he must have heard everything before, but I wanted him to get angry, to shout at me, to warn me of terrible punishments. But he just listened and whispered,

'Yes . . . Oh, dear now . . . Yes . . .'

And then he forgave me, told me to pray for purity, and gave me a penance of Our Fathers, Hail Marys, Glory Bes. It was too easy. Even as I said the penance, kneeling at the altar rail, I knew it would happen again, and I wanted to be punished for it properly, before it became worse.

The dreams of course were about women and girls, about any woman or any girl who had caught my eye during the day.

In the effort to displace these dreams, and to supplement the penances of Father O'Mahoney, I spent many of these nights bringing to mind the day of Barbara's death. Late winter, an unblemished morning, sun streaming in at my window, a chorus of songbirds, silence in the house. Still early, 7 a.m. The day before me stretching endless and unused and filled with hope. And then movement, Mam rising, her awful, awful cry. Our poorly sister wouldn't wake, couldn't wake, was already gone to God. Our mother pursued her, called after her, begged her, gripped our sister in her arms and refused to relinquish her. Colin, Catherine and I gathered at the fringes, useless. A whole morning of prayer and protest and lamentation, till such silence, and despite the sunlight such darkness, fell again. The doctor was allowed to confirm our sister's death, Father O'Mahoney to pray over her. We stumbled from the corners, Mam let us and Dad into her arms, and we wept together and held our cold and long-gone little sister in our useless arms.

The dreams changed. One night my head was filled with a kind of fluttering. I turned towards it and saw an angel landing in my dark. She came towards me, floating rather than walking. She was clothed only in white fire, and her wings stood high behind her, covered in pure white feathers, like those of doves. Through the fire I could see her body, shaped like any woman's, but more beautiful than any woman's. Without speaking, she came to me and I felt her fire all over and inside me. I lay stunned, watching her wings beating gently above us, pure white against the dark.

I told Father O'Mahoney. He listened in silence. Then there was concern in his voice.

'The tricks of the Devil,' he said. 'They will adopt the most exquisite of shapes. Resist them all. Be firm.'

I said my penances. But I was far gone. I knew that my angel would come again, that again she would be wonderful, the most wonderful thing I'd known. Night after night she came to wrap me in her fire, and I welcomed her, embraced her, though I knew she was leading me to Hell.

One night, after she'd been with me for hours, her wings began to beat more quickly and I felt myself being lifted. I held on tight, gazed into her perfect face as we began to fly through the gentle winds of the dark. She kept looking down at me, smiling to reassure me. We travelled for an age, until the dark began to change and we entered a pink dawn that slowly changed to white until the light itself was her fire, and she was so absorbed by it that I could no longer see her. I knew she was there only by feeling her tight in my arms, and by the continued rhythmic beating of her wings. I looked from side to side, wanting to see where we were, but there was only the fire on all sides, going on for ever.

I woke in my crumpled bed. There was frost on the window, snow outside. I closed my eyes tight, wanting the angel again, but I was awake, it was ordinary daylight, and she was gone.

I didn't confess it. I told myself it was just a dream, nothing to do with becoming bad. I just told the old dreams, the old women and girls. Father O'Mahoney said, 'Remember that the body is God's temple, and each of us is forever in God's thoughts.'

The next time, it started like snow falling, a thousand flakes falling from the darkness, each flake a glowing white flame. Then I saw the wings, and beneath the wings the bodies, each one a woman's, but more beautiful than any woman's. A whole flight of angels landed in my dark.

The angel I knew came to me first. Then the others one by one came to join her, until there were a thousand angels with me, and wherever I turned was filled with their white fire, their tender faces, their brilliant bodies, their beating wings.

We went together, all of us, through the winds of the dark, a fiery swarm with me at the centre, until we entered the pink again and then the white. They peeled away from me there, leaving me the one blemish in all that white. I threw my arms out frantically, striking wings and faces and hair, until my hand was taken and the angel drew me towards her and laid her arm across my shoulder.

'Don't worry,' she whispered, and I could tell by the way she spoke that she was smiling. 'There's someone to see you.'

She took my hands and stretched then out into the brightness. My fingertips encountered skin, hair, eyes, a tender cheek. I felt the lips part, felt breath breaking into laughter.

'Barbara,' I gasped. 'Barbara.'

I reached down, I lifted her, and at her back I felt the quick fluttering of her own small wings. She put her arms around my neck and kissed me and spoke my name.

'Oh, Barbara,' I gasped.

So much more I wanted to say. So much more I wanted to cry out. But I became speechless. I could only hold her, feel her as happy and tiny as she always was, feel the life continuing to burn and sparkle in her.

'You see?' she said, and her voice was filled with delight. 'You see? I'm all right. Everything's all right.'

Then she was gone, suddenly, flying out into the light and I knew there was no way to follow her.

'You see?' the angel whispered. 'You see?'

'But how . . . ?' I said. 'How?'

She pressed a finger to my lips.

'Come with me,' she said. 'But never say a word.'

We moved forward, and the white fire burned even more brightly, so brightly that I had to close my eyes against it. When we stopped, she whispered, 'Listen.'

I could hear nothing, only my own breathing and the beating of my heart.

'Listen.'

I started to ask what I should listen for, but then I heard it. Further into the fire, someone else was breathing. Long breaths in and long breaths out, filled with low groans, soft rattling and whistling sounds.

'Hear it?'

'Yes.'

She turned me away, and we went back, to where I could open my eyes again.

'What was it?' I asked.

'That was God, fast asleep. He'll wake up soon. Hold on tight.'

Back we came through the pink and the black, and into my room's darkness where we came to rest. She giggled like Barbara had, and held me at arms' length, preparing to leave.

'Don't go,' I said.

'Everyone will wake up soon,' she said.

'When can I come back again?' I asked.

She touched my cheek and smiled and shook her head.

'One day,' she said. 'When you have your wings again.'

And for the last time she stayed with me, and the white fire that did not burn spread far into me, making me understand how it feels to be angelic. Then she was gone, diminishing to a snowflake, disappearing into the dark . . .

That day Mam did again what she so often did. She pulled my shoulders forward and kissed me.

'You're the bright one this morning,' she said.

I laughed.

I let her slip her fingers beneath my shoulder-blades.

'Where my wings were,' I said. 'Where they'll be again.'

She held me close.

'It's true,' she said. 'Even though you're growing up so fast you have to keep on knowing that it's true.'

I reached up and for the first time slipped my fingers beneath her own shoulder-blades.

'You as well,' I told her.

'Yes, me as well. All of us. Barbara, you, me, all of us. Everybody.'

And then we were silent, and we felt for a moment the fire within us burning, until Dad came in, and we giggled, imagining together the white feathers rising from his hairy back and beyond his balding head.

*   *   *

It was the first time I had asked Father O'Mahoney anything, and it was the first time he became angry.

'If we're like this when we're in God's thoughts,' I said. 'What are we like when we're in his dreams?'

His hand struck the thin screen between us. He shouted at my blasphemy and gave me five decades of the rosary to say. I didn't say them, though. I knew that God slept, that even angels weren't always good, that

265

I'd have my wings back one day, and that dreams were only dreams.

ACKNOWLEDGEMENTS

Some of these stories have been previously
published/broadcast as follows:

Behind the Billboards, *Northern Stories
7* (Arc Publications). Buffalo Camel
Llama Zebra Ass, *Edinburgh Review*.
Chickens, *Sleepless Nights* (Iron Press).
Counting the Stars, *Northern* Stories 6
(Arc Publications); BBC Radio 4.
Jonadab, *Panurge*. Loosa Fine, *London
Magazine*. My Mother's Photographs,
The Echo Room Yearbook; BBC
Radio Newcastle. The Baby, *Critical
Quarterly*. The Fusilier, *Iron*. The
Middle of the World, *Pretext* (EAS
Publishing). The Time Machine, The
Bridport Prize Anthology. Where Your
Wings Were, BBC Radio 4; A Kind of
Heaven (Iron Press).

The extracts on pages 131 and 132
from *The Third Eye* by T. Lobsang
Rampa are used with kind permission
from the estate of Sarah Anna Rampa.